Meet P

Her special
is lau

 Penny has
Mills & Boon® for twenty years, from her
home in Cheshire where she lives with her
husband, three dogs, and two cats. Brought up in
Preston, Lancashire, Penny's family moved to
Cheshire when she was seventeen. She started her
working life as a secretary in a bank, but had always
told and written stories for herself and her family.

After reading an article in a magazine about
how Mills & Boon were looking for new writers, she
submitted a story just out of curiosity. With very few
amendments, that first submission was published,
and one hundred novels later, what started as a
hobby is now a way of life.

'All my books are special at the time of writing,'
says Penny, 'which means I don't have favourites.
I have left it up to the editors at Mills & Boon to tell
me which have been most popular,
and which should go into the
Collector's Edition, because what
matters is what my readers like.'

MILLS & BOON

Penny Jordan

COLLECTOR'S EDITION

You Owe Me

*Look out for this exciting
'Collector's Edition' over
the coming months*

At first there had been times when the growing resemblance between father and son had caught her unawares.

At times that small face had uncannily adopted a once familiar expression which had resurrected deeply buried, half-forgotten memories. And for some time now she had been bracing herself for when Jacey started asking about his father…

Kate Proctor is part Irish and part Welsh, though she spent most of her childhood in England and several years of her adult life in Central Africa. Now divorced, she lives just outside London with her two cats, Florence and Minnie (presented to her by her two daughters who live fairly close by).

Having given up her career as a teacher on her return to England, Kate now devotes most of her time to writing. Her hobbies include crossword puzzles, bridge and, at the moment, learning Spanish.

THE UNSUSPECTING FATHER

BY
KATE PROCTOR

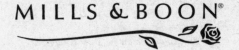

MILLS & BOON®

First published in Great Britain 1998
Harlequin Mills & Boon Limited,
Eton House, 18-24 Paradise Road, Richmond, Surrey TW9 1SR

© Kate Proctor 1998

ISBN 0 263 80821 1

Set in Times Roman 11 on 12 pt.
01-9806-50155 C1

Printed and bound in Great Britain
by Mackays of Chatham PLC, Chatham

CHAPTER ONE

EVERYTHING was going to be all right, Beth Miller chanted mechanically to herself as the door of the medical director's office closed behind her. She took a deep breath, the subtle stylishness of her surroundings lost on her as the events of the past few hours began hammering out their effect on her. She had been fine on the way down—worried, of course, but fully in control of herself. But now that control was in danger of being stripped from her.

She walked over to the window, a tall, willowy figure dressed in a deceptively simple chocolate and gold silk shift dress, her tawny gold hair twisted high on her head in casual elegance. Outwardly she remained the successful model, coolly composed, delicately beautiful; inwardly she was having difficulty coming to terms with the reason why she was standing here in this up-market, state-of-the-art clinic in Palma... Palma, the capital of the island to which she had once vowed she would never return yet which had been her home for the past five years.

But her home proper was in Pollensa, up in the north of the island, not down here in the south, where nothing was familiar, where— She cut her straying thoughts off abruptly. She had to calm down; it was delayed shock doing this to her, she told herself firmly. It was upsetting not to be able to use her local hospital, but this one came with the highest recommendations... And everything *was* going to be all right.

'Beth?'

She froze, that utterance of the single syllable of her name plucking a chord in the darkest recesses of her being.

'Good God, it *is* you!'

Deep and softly accented, the voice washed over her, its utter familiarity freezing the blood in her veins. It had to be her imagination, she told herself as a tremor of disbelief blasted through her. She had had a worse shock than she had realized—and now her mind was playing this most terrible of tricks on her!

She swung round in a panic of denial, unable to accept that the moment she had refused even to contemplate for six years had arrived—and at this of all times.

But now, like the embodiment of the worst nightmare imaginable, Jaime Caballeros was walking towards her.

'When I was given the name Miller, I naturally wondered.' The voice, resonant with its unforgettable tinge of huskiness, again washed over her. 'But I decided it was probably just a coincidence.'

A thousand words of protest shrieked out inside Beth as she opened her mouth to reply. 'Unfortunately for both of us, it wasn't.' Staggered by the cool composure of that completely unplanned utterance, Beth looked him full in the face. It was the memories that came tumbling into her head, as their gazes locked, that knocked the breath from her. Sensation after paralysing sensation raced through her as she searched for the miraculous changes that would render that unforgettable face comfortingly unfamiliar... She searched in vain. In his bearing there was still that air of aloofness, bordering on arrogance, that had always set him apart; and above all there was still the heart-stopping beauty of those perfectly sculpted features.

'Unfortunately? I sincerely hope not.' Anger flashed briefly in his eyes, utterly negating the calm detachment of his words.

No, thought Beth, feeling as though she would suffocate; nothing had changed... Least of all those sultry brown eyes with their flecks of a green that could turn from the sparkle of emerald to the turbulent darkness of a storm-tossed sea when passion possessed him. She gave an unconscious shake of her head, desperate to be free of such thoughts. 'Look, I'm afraid you haven't caught me at a good time.' Again she was startled to hear the composure in words she was scarcely aware of uttering as she tore her gaze from the unnerving effect of those eyes. 'I'm expecting a consultant here at any moment.'

'I know you are,' he stated quietly. 'I am that consultant.'

Beth felt herself sway, then the steadying grasp of hands on her shoulders.

'I think it's best if you sit down,' said Jaime, guiding her over to two leather armchairs flanking a low table in a corner of the room. After urging her down onto one, he seated himself on the other.

Beth took a deep breath in an attempt to calm herself, but her mind had become a jangling chaos of confusion and denial.

'Beth, would you like me to send for something for you to drink? Coffee—or perhaps something cold?'

She shook her head, her movements tense and

jerky. 'I don't want anything!' she exclaimed, her voice hoarse with strain. 'All I want is to know whether or not Dr Perez's diagnosis of appendicitis has been confirmed.'

'It has,' he replied. 'The examination your son had on admission confirms that he is suffering almost text-book symptoms of appendicitis.'

'And they'll have to operate?' whispered Beth, the words 'your son' bouncing off the walls of her mind and reverberating confusingly in her head. Had he sons and daughters of his own now? she wondered as she often had before. He and that woman whose name she had never known?

'Yes. Probably the day after tomorrow,' he replied, the detached professionalism in his tone mercifully disrupting her discomfiting train of thought. 'Beth, I'm sure your own doctor will have given you all the reassuring facts, though I dare say that's not going to stop you—like any mother with a sick child—being worried out of your mind. But I'm here to explain anything you're unsure of and to answer any questions you may care to ask.' He paused, his jaw tightening as his eyes flicked over Beth's averted face. 'If you would rather speak to another surgeon, I can easily arrange it.'

'It doesn't bother me who I speak to,' lied Beth, now feeling limp and slightly nauseous from the effort of trying to bring coherence to the fragmented mishmash churning in her mind. 'I just need the facts.'

He nodded and, using those same unrushed professional tones, he took her through the surgical procedures, paraphrasing himself in laymen's terms whenever he felt she might not have understood.

Because something that meant more to her than life

itself depended on his words, Beth was able to smother her feelings of utter incredulity and take in his every utterance. But there was a part of her that had broken away, dwelling exclusively on the man saying those words.

She could see now that the intervening years had brought subtle changes to his appearance. The soft edges of the younger man's features had now matured to an almost harsh strength. Attractive though he had been at twenty-six, at thirty-two there was a darkly brooding hint of danger in his looks that now made him devastatingly so. And she became aware of the changes in herself, in the small things that she noticed.

Six years ago she would have been incapable of recognizing the designer cut of the dark linen trousers he was wearing, or the exceptional quality of his silk shirt. No—six years ago she had had none of the useless knowledge she had since acquired... Then, in her innocent ignorance, she had simply loved him—loved him body and soul and with every shred of her being.

When he had finished, he paused. 'Is there anything more you feel you'd like to know?'

'No, you seem to have covered everything.' It didn't seem to matter what was going on in her head, she noted with dazed relief; she was still managing to string together reasonably intelligible words.

'Well, if you think of anything later, please don't hesitate to let me know.'

'That's very kind of you,' stated Beth stiffly. 'Thank you.'

'I believe your child's grandmother is with him at the moment.'

Beth felt shock ripple through her. Dear God, was this really happening to her? 'Yes.'

'It must be a comfort having her with you at a time like this.'

'I don't know what I'd do without her,' replied Beth coolly, despite the heat of the uncertainty raging within her. What had he seen? What did he know?

'Normally I would have examined your son before speaking to you like this, but I was called out to an emergency and only arrived back a short while ago,' he explained, as though answering her silent questions. 'All I've had time for is to speak briefly with the paediatric team that examined him. I'm afraid I don't know what age your son is—or even his name.'

'His name is Jacey,' she stated, unable to keep the naked hostility from her tone… Jaime Carlos—named in one crazy, despairing moment of madness after his father.

'An unusual name.'

'Perhaps it is,' she retorted, fighting to ward off the increasing sensation that this couldn't possibly be happening to her. 'But that's his name.'

'And he's how old?'

'He's five—he was five in April,' she said, looking him full in the eye.

There was no way he could disguise the sudden tensing of his body, nor the swift draining of colour from his face. He did make a belated attempt to hide the naked fury that burned in his eyes, but he left it too late and what she saw shook Beth to the core of her being… The same fury had burned in his eyes that day, six long years ago, and the memory of it had come close to destroying her.

'I can assure you, Beth, he will receive the best possible care here.'

'I'm sure he will,' muttered Beth woodenly. Of

course he would, she told herself in desperation as her mind at last accepted that this was no nightmare, but reality. But the knowledge that she was again having to put her trust in the man who had once brutally shattered it was tearing her apart.

'You don't sound completely convinced,' he observed warily. 'Beth, if you have a problem dealing with me it's better—'

'I don't find that a problem in the least.' The lie blasted from her, cutting off his words. 'Better the devil you know—isn't that so, Jaime? And whatever else you may be I have no doubt you're a very fine doctor.'

'Beth, we can't—' He broke off as the telephone on the desk rang. He walked over and picked up the receiver, announcing himself. 'Yes, that's fine,' he said in Spanish. 'And some coffee wouldn't go amiss. Thank you.' He turned towards Beth. 'There are a few routine tests that need to be carried out on your little boy, so his grandmother is joining us here.' He glanced at his watch. 'I can stay for a while to answer any questions she may have, but if you would prefer to be alone with—'

'No—please… I—I'd rather you stayed,' stammered Beth, her desire that Rosita receive the benefit of his professional reassurances overriding all other considerations. 'She'll probably ask all the questions I should have.'

'Beth, you're doing fine,' he stated, the faintest ghost of a smile for the first time touching his mouth. 'It's all very well for us doctors droning on about how little there is for you to worry about, but as a mother you're bound to—'

He broke off at the sound of a knock on the door. 'Come in.'

Beth glanced over and saw a woman enter bearing a tray. She leapt to her feet when she caught sight of the plump, motherly figure of a second woman. 'Rosita!' she cried, racing across the room and hurling herself into familiar, comforting arms.

'If only you could have been spared this, my darling,' whispered the Spanish woman anxiously, plainly already in possession of the facts; then she turned to face Jaime.

Beth turned too and saw Jaime's expression of incredulity as he looked at the older woman.

'Señora Rubio?' he croaked, as though unable to believe his eyes.

'Yes,' replied Rosita, releasing Beth and stepping towards Jaime, her eyes scrutinizing his bemused face. 'I only learned the name of the proprietor of this clinic a few minutes ago,' she stated candidly, leaving him in no doubt that it was a name she recognized.

Jaime gave a brief, formal bow, then approached her, his hand outstretched.

As they went through the ritual of formally shaking hands, Beth's still befuddled mind struggled to understand Jaime's reaction to Rosita. As the widow of one of Spain's most renowned painters, Rosita was well-known. What was also well-known was the fact that the plane crash that had tragically taken the life of Miguel Rubio had also cruelly taken that of his twenty-year-old daughter Manolita—the only child of the Rubios. Jaime knew both her parents were dead, Beth reminded herself before a groan of disbelief escaped her as the identity of the grandmother Jaime had been expecting suddenly dawned on her.

'Are you all right, Beth?' demanded Rosita, racing back to her side.

Beth nodded, incapable of speech as tears suddenly overwhelmed her.

'I'm afraid my presence hasn't made a difficult time any easier for Beth,' stated Jaime with matter-of-fact candour. 'But please let me assure you, Señora, as I have Beth, that your...that the little boy will receive the best possible care here.'

'I have no doubt of that,' replied Rosita, flashing Beth an unguardedly anxious look. 'I've been told that the appendicitis has definitely been confirmed.'

'It has,' agreed Jaime. 'Let me go over what I've just been explaining to Beth.'

By the time he had finished, Beth had just about mastered her tears, though her state of mind remained one of seesawing confusion.

'I'm sorry,' she sniffed into the handkerchief Rosita had produced for her. 'I—'

'Sorry?' snorted the Spanish woman indignantly, leading her back to her seat and taking the one next to it. 'A good cry never hurt anyone.'

'And perhaps a good strong coffee also?' enquired Jaime, having poured the coffee, now bringing them a cup each, black and scalding.

As he handed Rosita hers he smiled and it was in that moment that she began to understand, as she had never quite before, just what it was that had broken Beth's heart and left it irreparable for all those years. Her discovery that it was this man who owned the clinic had shaken her badly, but, having spoken to him, she felt her worries inexplicably lessening and found herself wondering why.

Much of what she knew about Jaime Caballeros

was hearsay, she fretted to herself, but there were also several facts. There was the fact of his thoroughly aristocratic background, visible now, even without prior knowledge, in that air of aloof, almost arrogant self-possession he exuded. Though she had never said anything to Beth, in her heart of hearts she had suspected that the gulf in their social status, of which the young English girl had seemed so touchingly oblivious, had played a part in his ruthless abandonment of her.

And then there was the fact that she knew at least one of the numerous stories of other hearts he had broken to be true—something which, again, she could never have brought herself to discuss with Beth... Yet when he smiled, thought Rosita with a pang, that extraordinarily handsome face became transformed and, search though she did, she could see nothing but the openness of purity in it... She was seeing Jacey in all his innocence.

'Señora, if there are any other questions you wish to ask,' he said, misinterpreting the unconscious intensity of her gaze, 'please don't hesitate to do so.'

'I have no more questions for the moment,' she replied, thrown by the disturbingly ambivalent feelings she was experiencing towards the man who had come so close to destroying the girl she loved as a daughter. It was that wretched sixth sense of hers going into overdrive, she thought exasperatedly, before comforting herself with the reminder that, where people were concerned, it had yet to fail her. Her eyes met Beth's and it pained her to see how drained she was looking. 'We're certain Jacey couldn't be in better hands than he is here,' she said encouragingly.

'Of course we are,' agreed Beth—compared to

Jacey's well-being, all other considerations were as nothing.

'Instead of subjecting the little boy to yet another doctor, I'll have a word with the team seeing him now and postpone having a look at him until the morning,' said Jaime. 'There are probably things you both wish to discuss and I have a patient I want to look in on.' He gave a small, formal bow. 'I shall be back in about half an hour, but if you need anything just pick up the telephone.'

The instant the door closed behind him, Rosita reached over and took one of Beth's hands in hers. 'Darling, I can hardly bear to think what it must have done to you, having to deal with him, of all people, under such circumstances,' she murmured sadly. 'But now we have to think only of Jacey and how we're going to handle this.'

'Jacey?' whispered Beth dazedly. 'My poor baby,' she choked. 'He was trying so hard to be brave...'

Rosita leapt to her feet as Beth's words deteriorated into a sob. Sitting herself down on the arm of Beth's chair, she took the weeping girl in her arms. 'Darling, he's going to be all right,' she soothed softly. 'You do know that, don't you?'

Beth nodded, trying to get a grip on herself. 'That's the only thing that I really feel certain about, thank God,' she whispered. 'But not about anything else,' she added, desperation in her words. 'Rosita, from the moment Jaime walked through that door, I haven't been able to think properly... It wasn't just that I'd had a shock and felt confused... I had no control over what was going on in my mind and whenever I said anything—'

'Beth, listen to me,' cut in Rosita sharply. 'Of

course it's shock! Yesterday you hadn't a care in the world—today you race down here in an ambulance and walk smack into your sick child's father... If that isn't enough to scramble your wits, I can't think what would be.'

'You're right,' sighed Beth. 'It's just that I'm going to need some time to get my head round it all.'

'I'm afraid time is something you simply don't have,' stated Rosita quietly, her expression tight with concern. 'From the way Jaime kept referring to "the little boy", it's clear you haven't yet managed to tell him the truth.'

'And I've no intention of doing so!' burst out Beth, feeling as though her world was collapsing around her.

'Darling, what on earth are you saying?' There was an expression of horror on Rosita's face as she stood up. 'Jacey's age alone will be enough—'

'No! He already knows his age,' Beth cut in distractedly. 'Rosita, can't you see? He has a wife and most likely other children to consider... Jaime won't *want* to know!'

'Dear God, this is turning into an absolute nightmare,' groaned Rosita, sinking back down onto the other chair. 'Darling, all these years, his was a name we so rarely mentioned and perhaps it wasn't so wise... Beth, there is no wife—no other children.'

Beth looked across at her with open disbelief.

'I could have told you four or more years ago that he'd never married,' continued the older woman sadly, 'but, quite apart from his name being virtually taboo, there didn't really seem any point.'

Beth strove to rein in the several thoughts skittering

around in her mind. 'Four years ago?' she queried hoarsely. 'He could still have married since.'

Rosita gave a weary shake of her head. 'His fiancée died within a couple of months of their becoming engaged,' she stated woodenly.

'Oh, Rosita...how dreadful!' Beth whispered in horror. 'But, even so, it was all those years ago... A man like him, he's bound to have found someone else.'

Rosita shifted uncomfortably. 'Oh, he found dozens of other women all right, and by all accounts left a trail of broken hearts a mile long behind him by the time he took off for South America.'

'Rosita, how on earth do you know all this?' exclaimed Beth, completely thrown, not so much by what she was hearing but who she was hearing it from.

'And well you may ask, given that you know exactly how I feel about gossip,' sighed the Spanish woman. 'But for a while there was so much of it around I was only too glad you were away on assignments so often. It even got into the press—' She broke off, shaking her head. 'I don't know any of the details of his fiancée's death, but it would seem he took it hard... And consequently behaved very badly to other women.'

'Perhaps he was simply searching for someone who could take her place,' said Beth, still stunned by what she had heard.

Rosita hesitated, then decided that now simply wasn't the time to disclose the damning facts she possessed. 'Perhaps,' she conceded with grave reluctance. 'But the fact is that he hasn't married.'

'Oh, Rosita, when I think of the number of times

I've thought about Jacey having half brothers and sisters he would never know… Hating the very idea of it…'

'My poor love,' sighed Rosita. 'But the point is that Jaime has a son and you can't deny him the right of knowing that.'

'He has no rights as a father,' Beth exploded bitterly. 'He gave up all claim to them long before Jacey was born!'

'No, Beth, he was never given a choice where those rights were concerned and, no matter what, Jacey is his flesh and blood,' insisted Rosita. 'What if, God forbid, it came to a father operating in ignorance on his own son?'

Beth shook her head distractedly. 'I'd never let that happen, Rosita. I…I wouldn't do that, not even to him.'

'Of course you wouldn't,' murmured Rosita. 'But you—' She broke off, frowning. 'Did I imagine it, or did you say that he knows Jacey's age?'

Beth nodded, her heart lurching sickeningly. She had never been able to bring herself to tell anyone the full horror of her humiliation that last night all those years ago. The only other person who knew was Cisco Suarez, a young student working as a barman, who had befriended her in her anguished hour of need. Jaime had plainly assumed that the 'grandmother' concerned would be Cisco's mother, which was why he had been so thrown by Rosita's arrival.

'But he can't possibly think—'

'Oh, he can, Rosita, he can,' Beth cut in wearily. 'But, to be fair to him, only because I allowed him to. It makes me cringe even to think of it now. I was so twisted with hurt that last time I saw him…I wanted to hurt him back by letting him believe I'd been unfaithful to him. The only thing I hurt was his pride—he was only too happy to believe the lies I told him.'

'You were so young, so terribly vulnerable,' whispered Rosita sadly, her eyes brimming with tears.

'And look at me now,' teased Beth with a spark of her old self, hating to see the Spanish woman so upset.

'Yes, just look at you now,' responded Rosita with undisguised pride. 'Sometimes I get the feeling you don't fully appreciate what you've achieved. For someone who almost had to be dragged by the hair into modelling, you haven't done too badly. You're an international star, you… Don't you roll your eyes at me like that, my girl,' she chuckled as Beth did precisely that. 'Just how many twenty-five-year-olds do you think there are who could afford to retire in relative luxury, as you're now able to?'

'They paid me a ridiculous amount of money,' laughed Beth. 'And then most of those ultra-cautious investments I made became involved in take-over bids. It was sheer luck!'

'And luck is something you deserve a lot more of than you've had,' sighed Rosita. 'Darling, I wish I didn't have to go back to Pollensa tonight, but I really must. Tomorrow I'll see if I can make some arrangements regarding the gallery and—'

'No,' cut in Beth firmly. 'With Juanita due to go on holiday, you'll be needed there in the mornings. We'll stick to what we decided—that you come down in the afternoons when you can.'

'But—'

'But nothing,' chided Beth with a smile. 'It would

be different if Jacey were in here for anything more serious than a routine operation, but he isn't. So, if you go changing all your plans it'll be because of me, not Jacey—and I'm not having that.'

'Of course I'd be changing them because of you!' exclaimed Rosita candidly, flashing her a troubled look. 'You know what you have to do, darling…but my worry is, will you do it?'

'You don't have to worry,' replied Beth hoarsely, a band of misery tightening round her heart as her mind recoiled from even contemplating telling Jaime he had a son. 'I promise you, Rosita.'

'We'll say no more about it, then,' stated the older woman quietly. 'What we really should have done, though, is get you booked into—' She broke off as the door opened and Jaime walked in.

'I've just had a word with the paediatric registrar,' he announced, walking over to them. 'Jacey's sound asleep and settled for the night.' He glanced from one to the other. 'I realize that the paediatric wing of your local hospital being temporarily closed can only have added to your problems. I was wondering what your plans were while Jacey's here.'

'I'll be returning to Pollensa now and driving down in the afternoons whenever I can. Beth, of course, wishes to remain down here during Jacey's stay,' replied Rosita. 'I was just about to suggest to her that we see about finding a hotel for her.'

'There's really no need for you to be driving up and down the length of the island like that, nor for Beth to be looking for hotels,' he stated firmly. 'My house here is entirely at your disposal and for as long as you both need it.'

'Speaking for myself, I'd happily take you up on

your kind offer,' stated Rosita quietly, 'but I'm afraid
I'll be needed in my gallery most mornings.'

'I understand… But my offer is still open to Beth.'
He glanced at Beth, as though expecting her to react.
When she gave no indication of even having heard
him, he frowned then continued addressing Rosita.
'Visiting is unrestricted here, so it would be far easier
coming and going from my house than from a hotel.
I also have a priority line between the house and here,
which Beth could use whenever she wished.'

Rosita reached out a hand to Beth, who seemed lost
in a private world of her own. 'I suppose it is rather
late to set about looking for somewhere,' she murmured hesitantly. She turned to look at Beth, any last
doubts she had swept aside by the look of drained
exhaustion she encountered. 'And something Beth
could plainly do without,' she added firmly. 'It's most
kind of you—thank you very much.'

'I was wondering if you had eaten,' said Jaime, his
eyes flicking with professional concern over Beth's
silent figure.

Rosita glanced down at her watch, then rose to her
feet. 'I think it's best if I get on my way,' she said.
'But Beth could probably do with some food—she's
eaten practically nothing all day… Beth?'

Beth gave a dazed shake of her head and stood up.
It wasn't that she hadn't been taking in what had been
going on around her, it was just that her still unreli-
able thought processes had kept being interrupted by
her mind's constant replaying of her son's name, uttered for the first time by his father. 'I'm sorry, I was
miles away,' she apologized, and forced a reassuring
smile to her lips as Rosita gave her an anxious look.
'I think everything's just started to catch up with

me…and the fact that I am rather hungry probably isn't helping.' She hesitated, a feeling of having completely lost her bearings flooding through her. 'But first I…I'd just like to pop in and say goodnight to Jacey… On my own.'

'And while you do that there's something I'd like to ask Señora Rubio's advice about,' said Jaime. 'We'll meet you in the foyer.'

As Beth made her way back to the paediatric wing, she wondered about the advice Jaime wanted from Rosita, but only in passing.

It was only when she was actually at her son's bedside that she felt a semblance of peace and order return to her mind. Resisting an almost overwhelming urge to gather his sleeping little form into her arms, she leaned over and brushed her lips against his cheek, wonder at the beauty and love that were a living part of herself bringing a choking sensation to her. To her he was perfection personified, the reason why—had she the power to turn back the clock—there was no way on earth she would ever choose to erase the brief, devastating presence of Jaime Caballeros from her life.

From the moment she had known she was carrying a life within her, the love had begun, sustaining and protecting her from the ravages of her desolation, just as she had sustained and protected that growing life.

Studying the small face in the glow of the night light, she saw a miniature replica of the features she had come to hate with a passion as fierce as the love she had once borne their possessor. At first there had been times when the growing resemblance would catch her unawares, choking the breath in her, as the small face uncannily adopted a once familiar expression, when those green-flecked eyes, mercifully less eloquent than those of his father, would unexpectedly resurrect a deeply buried, half-forgotten memory.

As time had passed and Jacey's own character had developed, those disturbing moments had all but disappeared, aided by her certainty that her son's beauty was as deep as his warm, outgoing little heart and that, even when he was at his most obnoxious, there was nothing of his father's ruthless duplicity to be found in his nature.

For some time now, she had been bracing herself for when he started asking about his father. She knew she was taking the coward's way out by telling herself she would base her answers on how he phrased his questions when the time actually came. But he had thrown her, shortly before his last birthday, not with questions of his father, but by informing her he would like a baby brother or sister. A lump came to her throat as she remembered the earnestness with which he had assured her he wasn't in the least fussy about which it was. Her eyes were luminous with love as she gazed down at him. Yes, his request had certainly thrown her, she thought with a small shiver of remembered shock, but not as much as her own reaction to it. For one heart-stopping instant she had been gripped by a raw and primitive desire for another child and had been left feeling shaken and confused.

Her heart filled as she took one last look at him before leaving. Tomorrow, another pair of eyes would have the right to regard Jacey as a son, however reluctantly...but for now he was still hers and hers alone.

CHAPTER TWO

FOR one brief moment, as she watched Rosita's car drive away, Beth was gripped by a need to run after it and beg her not to go.

'Come, let's find my car and then get some food into you.'

Beth turned and saw Jaime pick up the holdall she had taken from Rosita's car and found herself wondering vaguely what it was about his voice that made it so distinctive—that had made it so instantly recognizable after all these years.

'Beth?'

'I'm not hungry,' she stated, following along behind him in the shadowy darkness of the car park.

'You said you were earlier,' he said, a slight frown creasing his brow as his eyes skimmed over her slim figure.

'I only said that to please Rosita,' replied Beth with a shrug as they reached a large, low-slung car in gleaming dark green. 'She worries if I don't eat regularly.'

'She obviously takes great care of you,' he murmured, opening the passenger door for her. 'You're lucky.'

'Yes, I am—very,' agreed Beth a few moments later, leaning back against the rich leather upholstery and closing her eyes. 'I don't know what I'd have done without her,' she added, but there was no bitterness in her words—they were merely a statement of fact. And she had made Rosita a promise, she thought as her mind gave in and faced the subject numbing it with apprehension. It was her duty, if nothing else, to tell him about Jacey. But how? Getting the words together in her mind would be a daunting enough task... But actually finding what it would take to utter them...

'There's a good tapas bar not too far from here,' he told her once they were out of the clinic grounds, his tone cool and oddly formal. 'Perhaps that would appeal to you more than a proper meal.'

'I told you—I'm not hungry.'

'Well, I am,' he told her with a hint of acerbity, 'and I'd rather not have Señora Rubio accusing me of neglecting you.'

Beth's mind was too preoccupied with trying to form the words she would later have to utter to respond, and it was in that same state of preoccupied silence that, a few minutes later, she followed him into a small, spotless tavern.

She was still lost in her search for those words when he ordered coffee and tapas, but she hadn't come up with a single one by the time the food arrived.

As the silence between them grew and became charged, Beth found herself remembering other meals they had shared, remembering when it was always the power of their insatiable need for one another that had charged the atmosphere between them. In an attempt to distract herself from this disturbing train of thought she helped herself to some of the food. She began eating and found the distraction had worked, except that now the ache of an unbearable sadness filled her.

'Well, it's a relief to see that you actually do eat,'

said Jaime, his eyes coolly observant. 'I've heard of women in your profession being forced to exist on lettuce leaves for fear of adding the odd milligram or two to their weight.'

'Have you really?' retorted Beth, almost choking on the anger flaring in her; he had managed to make it sound as though he regarded what she did as tantamount to being on the streets. 'Well, luckily for me, I happen to be one of those people who can eat whatever she likes without gaining weight. It just so happens that, at the moment, I have rather a lot on my mind and don't feel like pigging out as I would normally.'

The ghost of a smile touched his lips. 'I've obviously offended you,' he murmured. 'And that truly wasn't my intention.' Neither the smile nor the apology that had followed it had managed to reach his watchful eyes. 'You have done incredibly well for yourself, Beth. I doubt if there's a country in the world that hasn't your face on a hoarding and its magazines filled with images of you.'

Now he was managing to make her sound like some ghastly pandemic disease, thought Beth angrily, popping a bite-sized tapas into her mouth to stop herself retaliating.

'So, what happened to your plans to learn Spanish and teach the underprivileged in South America?' he drawled softly.

'My son happened,' she informed him frigidly, hating him for mocking the dream that had sustained her throughout her barren teenage years and for resurrecting the memories now filling her mind. Jacey had been only a few months old when the full extent of her earning potential as a model had become clear to

her. It was only then that she'd realized that it had
been her pride, not the spectre of Jaime, that had held
her back from taking the step of making Mallorca her
home.

There could be few families closer than the lov-
ingly knit unit she, Rosita and Jacey had become, and
with her new-found financial independence she had at
last been free to take the only step both logic and her
heart decreed. But always there had been that fear, at
the back of her mind, of running into Jaime, despite
the knowledge that he worked in Madrid.

It had been almost two years before a chance spot-
ting of his name in a newspaper article had brought
her release from that fear. She had begun reading it
in trepidation of learning he was to return to Mallorca
from Madrid, but had discovered instead that he had
gone to South America. She had discarded the article
at that point, without finishing it.

Jaime leaned back suddenly, dragging his hands in
a gesture of weariness down his face. 'I'm sorry,
Beth,' he muttered. 'It's been a tough day for you and
I'm not helping.' He reached across the table towards
the small hand stroking the rim of her saucer in edgy
restlessness. He terminated the action before it was
completed, dropping his hand to the table, the long,
artistic fingers drumming lightly against the dark
wood.

Beth looked down at his slim, tanned fingers,
watching as those of his other hand came to join and
entwine with them…watching and remembering how
those now clasped hands had once caressed every inch
of her body in the frenzied heat of shared passion.

She took a rasping breath, stifling the cry of horrified protest that almost burst from her as the white-hot heat of sexual longing seared through her.

'What would *you* know about what today's been like for me?' she demanded, panicked into aggression by the questioning look with which he had responded to her sudden gasp.

'Not having children of my own, I admittedly don't have firsthand experience, but—' He broke off with an exclamation of impatience. 'Damn it, Beth! We both know what this is really about. Now or in ten years, it was never going to be easy when we ran into one another again!'

'I have no interest whatsoever in dredging up the past,' Beth responded coldly.

'And neither have I,' he retorted, 'which is why I hope you won't take offence if I ask you if you're married.'

'I'm not married,' she blurted out, completely thrown by the question.

'I ask because I happen to know that Francisco Suarez is back here on holiday,' he stated tonelessly. 'But perhaps you're already aware of that.'

Beth picked up her coffee cup, her hands shaking so badly she had to resort to using both of them for fear of spilling the contents. She pressed the cup to her lips as she fought to gain some semblance of control. It was his absolute, unquestioning certainty that Cisco was Jacey's father that she was finding so devastating. To be fair to him, he had been scrupulous about taking precautions, but Jacey had none the less been conceived. What had happened was an accepted fact of life, she reflected numbly, yet Jaime, for all his medical training, appeared to be in complete ignorance of it. Or was he simply hedging his bets against the unthinkable; giving her warning of how implacably closed his mind was even to contemplation of it?

'Clearly you'd rather the subject were dropped,' he snapped through the silence, a chilling bleakness glittering in his eyes. 'Forget I ever brought it up.'

'But you did,' Beth pointed out icily, anger and a terrible desolation churning within her.

For several seconds he scowled across the table at her, the veneer of civility he had so unsuccessfully tried to maintain towards her now stripped from him. He gave a sudden, angry shake of his head, then picked up his cup and drank from it.

'Beth, this is all so wrong,' he sighed, the anger draining from his face. 'The last thing I wanted was to dredge up painful memories for you... Please, you must believe that.'

As Beth looked over into that beautiful face, suddenly so earnest, so utterly sincere, she was alarmed to feel the beginnings of laughter quivering inside her. It had been a long, hard, hellish day, but at least now she had found a spark of humour in it. She wanted to tell him...to share the hilarious joke with him—that he, of all people, claimed to want to spare her painful memories. She wanted to tell him, but the laughter now erupting from her in soft, silvery peals prevented her.

Without a word Jaime rose and, slipping a leather billfold from his back pocket, threw some notes on the table.

'Come, Beth, we're going,' he told her quietly. When she showed no sign of having heard him, he yanked her still convulsed body to its feet and marched her out.

'Stop it, Beth! Please!'

By now Beth wanted to stop, was desperate to do so, but the more she tried, the more concerned his expression grew—and that struck her as the funniest sight she had ever seen in her life.

The stinging blow he delivered to the side of her face stopped the laughter instantly. It also momentarily distorted her ability to see things as they truly were because, for a single, fleeting moment, she saw a pain on his face as deep and destructive as any she had ever experienced herself.

With a groan that was like an echo of that pain, he pulled her into his arms. 'Beth, forgive me, but I had to do that... I had to stop you!'

The top of her head reached the curve of his chin and, as he held her against him, that was the inconsequential memory that surfaced in her mind. Then others followed—memories of his lean, hard body locked in passion with hers; memories of the incredible peace that had always come to her once their passion was spent.

'Are you all right now, Beth?'

He drew her head back until she was looking up into his eyes and what she saw instantly broke the spell. There was no pain, only the measured clinical gaze of the doctor inspecting a difficult patient.

'Of course I'm all right,' she replied coldly, stepping from him and towards his car, too drained and suddenly too exhausted to be bothered to give any thought to the spectacle she had just made of herself.

'It's just as well I wasn't capable of sharing the joke with you,' she flung at him almost petulantly as she got into the car, 'because you never would have seen the point.'

He got in and started up the car. 'Beth, despite what you might think, I meant what I said—the last thing I wanted to do was upset you.'

'No, I'm sure you didn't, Jaime,' she responded wearily, 'but at least I had a good laugh out of it.'

He flashed her a frowning look, but it wasn't until he turned the car into the grounds of a large house in the prestigious old area of the city that he spoke again. 'I rang earlier, so everything will be prepared for you.'

'Thank you,' muttered Beth.

She got out of the car, feeling as though she was about to drop with exhaustion, and waited while Jaime retrieved her holdall from the boot. She glanced up at the whitewashed, creeper-clad façade of the house, then over to where several huge urns nestled against sprawling bougainvillaeas, the geraniums that spilled in profusion from them lolling languidly in the moonlight. What in God's name was she doing here?

She looked, with an almost dazed detachment, at the man striding towards the front door, then followed after him. Standing a few paces behind him, she watched in silence as he unlocked the wrought-iron grille, then the carved double doors themselves.

When he closed the doors behind them, Beth found herself standing in a large hall, its walls a stark, almost dazzling white in contrast to the gleaming dark wood of the floor and the wide central staircase.

'First I'll show you your room,' said Jaime, her holdall still in his hand as he walked to the staircase.

As Beth followed him up the stairs to the galleried landing, it came to her why she was here. Rosita had suspected how long it would take before she could bring herself to tell Jaime the truth and wanted to be sure he would be at hand when the moment finally came. And sooner or later that moment had to come, she reminded herself apprehensively as Jaime opened one of the beautifully carved doors in a corridor off the gallery; she couldn't keep on chickening out like this.

'There's an adjoining bathroom,' Jaime informed her, placing her bag just inside the door. 'You should find everything you need prepared for you—if not, let me know.' He paused, a flicker of sympathy diluting the glittering coldness in his eyes as he looked down at her. 'This can't have been the easiest of days for you,' he said gently. 'Why don't you have a relaxing bath—or a shower, if you'd prefer—then join me downstairs for a mug of chocolate? I can run through the procedure regarding your son again, just in case there's anything you want clarified.'

'Thank you, I'd like that,' said Beth, some of the terrible tension easing from her as she accepted that when she joined him she would finally tell him. She stepped past him and through the door, hesitated, then turned to face him again. 'And thank you for letting me stay here; it…it's very kind of you.'

'Beth, you're welcome to stay here for as long as you wish,' he said. 'I really mean that.'

Before she could make any response the door had closed and she was alone.

The room was large, its heavy rosewood furniture traditionally simple in design and exquisitely carved. Again the walls were a cool stark white, while thick-piled rugs were scattered over the highly polished wood floor.

Beth closed her eyes momentarily, a sudden flash of awareness of the almost zombie-like state of mind she was in bringing a small stab of fear. The sooner she unpacked and showered, the sooner she would have the trauma of telling Jaime over and done with, she told herself firmly, picking up her holdall and placing it on an ornately carved chest at the foot of the huge, canopied bed.

Only moments after she had returned to the bedroom from showering, there was a knock at the door. She slipped into her dressing gown and opened the door.

Jaime was standing there, holding a small tray. 'I'm afraid something's cropped up,' he said. 'I have to go back to the clinic.' He handed her the tray. 'I've made you some chocolate.'

'That's very kind of you,' said Beth, taking the tray.

'Please feel free to familiarize yourself with the house and to help yourself to anything you need,' he said with formal politeness. 'I'd show you around myself, but I'm afraid I have to leave at once.'

Again, before Beth had any chance to respond, the door had closed and she was once more alone.

She walked over to the bed, placed the tray on the table beside it and sat down, feeling as though she had just been punched in the stomach. Though her initial reaction had been one of immeasurable relief, now she could only see the utter stupidity of such a response. The thought of the night ahead, with this still gnawing away at her, filled her with dread. But perhaps she wasn't the only one guilty of chickening out, she thought suddenly as she got into her nightdress and turned off the main light.

Her expression tight with bitterness, Beth climbed between the cool linen sheets and sat up against softly plump pillows. It had been a struggle for him even to be civil earlier, she reflected grimly, so the chances were he had decided he simply hadn't the stomach for any more of her company.

She picked up the mug and took a sip of the rich sweet chocolate, the darkness of an unbearable pain dulling her eyes as the barriers she had so painstakingly erected all those years ago came tumbling down and the memory of how much she had once loved him spread though her. Jaime's treachery had come so terrifyingly close to destroying her completely, she reflected numbly, that she had needed those barriers simply to preserve her sanity.

She closed her eyes as the memories came flooding back. In those first weeks of abject despair, when she had endlessly relived every instant of their relationship, she had been powerless to suppress the love that had burned undiminished in her right up until that inevitable memory of his pitiless betrayal. Her mind had remained a sickening seesaw of love and hatred until she had finally found the strength to remember him only as she had last seen him, his handsome face no longer familiar in its cold mask of loathing.

Naive and inexperienced as she had been at barely nineteen, she had never stood a chance, she reminisced bitterly; his performance had been brilliant.

But perhaps she had been more vulnerable than most, having been starved of love for so long, she thought, her eyes haunted as her mind was drawn back over the years...

A month after her eleventh birthday, her beloved parents had been cruelly taken from her in a road accident; ten months later, her paternal grandfather, whom she had adored and whose unstinting love had begun to restore the shattered pieces of her life, had died in his sleep of a massive heart attack. From then on her life had become a bleak, loveless existence under the guardianship of her grandfather's widow. Married relatively late in life to a widower several years her senior, Agnes Miller had made no attempt to hide her resentment of the child she irrationally held responsible for her sudden widowhood.

With Agnes's chilling inhospitality a barrier to forming any close friendships, Beth's only respite from a grindingly lonely regime had been her schooling. Starved of any other stimulus, she had avidly soaked up whatever came her way, seeking knowledge with an appetite that was almost obsessive.

At fourteen, her imagination fired by a school project on areas of social and educational deprivation in some of the Latin American countries, she had decided on her future. From then on her aim had been to obtain a degree in Spanish and Education, and to offer her skills to those so much less fortunate than herself... It was the dream she had clung to year in and year out, the dream that had lent purpose to the barren loneliness of her existence.

Then had come the scholarship that had opened up the world to her, giving her the chance to turn her dream into reality. University had been like another world—a world filled with opportunity and excitement. When one of the girls on her course had mentioned she would be spending the entire summer vacation improving her Spanish, courtesy of an old schoolfriend whose parents owned a large villa in Mallorca, she had been frank in her envy. When Lily, the other girl, had asked her to come along too, she had been greatly tempted.

'To be honest, you'd be doing me a favour,' Lily had coaxed. 'June can be a bit of an airhead at times and I've a feeling she and the other two who are going will want to do nothing but party all the time. Your Spanish accent's almost as bad as mine—just think what an opportunity this would be!'

From then on, her doubts dispelled, Beth had spent every weekend and three nights a week working in a busy local restaurant, earning every penny she could for her holiday.

Poor Lily, remembered Beth, tears sliding unnoticed down her cheeks; night after sleepless night of lying awake because of the raucous, unending parties without which June and her friends seemed to find life so dull had been more than she could take. Less than a week after their arrival, Lily had packed her bags and returned to England. But by then Jaime had entered Beth's life and while Jaime was in Formentor there had been no place on earth she would rather be.

Stifling a sob of protest as her memories again lit an urgent need in her, Beth reached over and switched out the bedside lamp. It was worse than it had been earlier in the bar, she thought in sickened panic. Now it was as though her body had no memory of the intervening years, yearning for him now with the same insatiable hunger with which it had once welcomed him.

She buried her face in the pillows, howling her despair into their softness. He was like a disease that had taken a terrible toll on her, she raged bitterly to herself. And one from which she had never fully recovered, judging by her inability to form relationships with other men. Just thinking about those other men—serious, intelligent and thoroughly decent—

made her heart ache for them. The pattern was always the same: the moment any man awakened physical attraction in her, a powerful, uncontrollable response was triggered, forcing her to terminate the relationship and leaving her hating herself for her inability to prevent herself punishing all men for the sins of Jaime Caballeros.

CHAPTER THREE

SUNLIGHT sneaking through louvred windows washed the room in its soft light, gently wakening Beth.

She lay motionless between the crispness of the linen sheets, her eyes drifting from one piece of beautifully carved furniture to the next as her mind made its reluctant journey from sleep to wakefulness. For an instant after the journey was completed, she panicked and tried to backtrack.

Then, angrily remonstrating with herself for being so pathetic, she swung her legs over the side of the bed and padded barefoot across the polished wood floor to the bathroom.

Yesterday had been a day of devastating shocks, resulting in last night's histrionic wallowing in misery. But that was all behind her now, she told herself firmly as she stepped under the shower. And it was pointless dithering around searching for the right words to tell Jaime about Jacey; they would come soon enough once she got started. She turned the powerful shower on to full blast as she felt her resolve waver and her stomach churn sickeningly.

She made her way back to the bedroom and began drying her hair, her resolve taking another dive at the sight of her wan, washed-out reflection in the mirror. She had tossed and turned, catnapping fitfully throughout the night—and it showed. She looked and felt like a zombie, she thought defeatedly, and she could chivvy herself till she was blue in the face, but nothing was going to change it.

She finished drying her hair, tied it up loosely, then slipped into a brightly patterned cotton dress, one she knew Jacey particularly liked because of its colours.

Feeling heavy-limbed and increasingly ill at ease, she left the room and went down the stairs to the hall. It was clearly a very large house and she hadn't the slightest idea of its layout. And then there would be Jaime's father, she remembered belatedly—unless he still spent most of his time in Barcelona... Jacey's grandfather.

A smile of sheer relief lit her face when a maid approached her at the foot of the stairs and offered to show her the way to the dining room.

'Beth,' murmured Jaime when she entered the room. His manner chillingly formal, he rose to his feet from the head of the long dining table with the languid grace that had once so captivated her. 'Did you sleep well?'

'Yes, thank you.' Despite her earlier good intentions, she was already succumbing to the eerie feeling that none of what was happening had anything to do with reality. She glanced around her, gripped by a sensation of utter detachment. The room was large, imposingly formal and was dominated by the long, highly polished dining table, set at one end only with heavy silver and delicate china. What she saw gave her a tiny glimpse into the world to which her son's father belonged—a far cry from her own humble beginnings. 'I'd like to get straight to the clinic, if that's convenient for you.'

'Of course,' he said, still standing. 'But first you

should have some breakfast,' he added, indicating the place laid to the left of his.

Beth walked the length of the table and sat down. 'I'll just have a coffee, thank you.'

'I could have some eggs boiled for you or—'

'No—this will do fine, thank you,' she interrupted, taking a sweet bun from a basket on the table.

'Are you sure?' he enquired, his expression guarded and noncommittal as he poured her some coffee. 'I seem to remember you used to find the Spanish predilection for sweet breakfasts somewhat strange.'

Beth ignored his words, but thanked him for the coffee he passed her. Things were bad enough without him dragging up the past, she thought bitterly.

'I'll make arrangements for a car and driver to be at your disposal any time I might not be available to run you between here and the clinic.'

'That's very kind of you,' said Beth, toying listlessly with the bun she had broken into several pieces as she tried to psych herself up to broach the subject tormenting her. 'Jaime, I... Yesterday, I...'

'Yesterday you what?' he asked, flashing her a wary look.

'I...I forgot about your father.' Words she hadn't intended came gushing from her. 'I hope my staying here isn't inconvenient for—'

'My father?' he interrupted, frowning. 'Beth, my father died almost three years ago.'

'I—I... Jaime, I'm so sorry,' she stammered, then picked up her cup and drank deeply to mask her disquiet. They hadn't been the words she'd intended, but now she felt dreadful, remembering how very close he had been to his father.

'Why should you be sorry?' he asked, bitterness edging his tone. 'You weren't to know.'

'But he couldn't have been very old.'

'No, he wasn't,' Jaime agreed brusquely. 'He was only fifty-six and the... No, as you say, he wasn't very old.'

Whatever he had been about to say, he had obviously changed his mind and he lapsed into a silence which continued for the rest of the meal and which, nerve-rackingly, he still hadn't broken by the time they got into his car.

He was plainly still deeply affected by his father's death, Beth told herself as they moved into the morning traffic, and the last thing she could do was break into his private grief to tell him about Jacey. Her thoughts began straying, reminding her that the dead man had a grandson he would never now see, a child that his son had yet to see.

She felt a shiver run through her and switched her attention to the man beside her for distraction. He had slipped a French navy linen jacket over his white short-sleeved shirt as they had left the house. One thing her career as a model had taught her, she reflected wryly, was how to spot good tailoring, and his was impeccable. Of course, she hadn't had any idea about things like that when she had first met him all those years ago, and the idea that their vastly different backgrounds might present a problem had never occurred to her... Which only went to show how pathetically naive she had been then, she thought bitterly.

'There's one thing I think we ought to discuss before we go inside,' said Jaime, cutting through her unwelcome thoughts as they entered the clinic grounds, 'and that's whether you'd feel happy with me operating on your son tomorrow.'

'No, Jaime,' she replied, feeling suddenly calm now that he had presented her with an opening. 'I wouldn't feel happy about it.' The instant the words were out, her fickle calm deserted her. 'Jaime, I have to—'

'No—that's fine by me,' he stated quietly, getting out of the car.

Beth scrambled out of her side. 'Jaime, *please,* I need to talk—'

'There's no need to say any more,' he assured her, his expression slightly amused as their eyes met across the roof of the car. 'A surgeon is a surgeon and we have several here who can be called on.'

'I'm glad to hear it,' Beth retorted stiffly, his amusement stirring angry resentment in her. 'But I have to tell you why.'

'Sorry to spoil your fun,' he drawled, his eyes glittering ice as they challenged hers, 'but I'm not in the least interested.'

A bitter fury churning in her, Beth turned on her heel and strode away.

'By the way, Beth,' he called to her as he followed her into the foyer, 'I have patients to see before I have another word with your son's team. I'll join you later.'

Beth slowed her steps as she made her way to Jacey's room, to allow time for her anger to subside. She now saw with terrible clarity at least one reason why she was having such difficulty telling Jaime…her fear of him flinging it back in her face and telling her he wasn't interested in the child who was her life. She gave an angry shrug—so what if he did? He was irrelevant to her and Jacey—he always had been and always would be.

The door of Jacey's room opened as she approached and a nurse stepped out.

'Señora Miller?' queried the young woman, smiling as she pulled the door to behind her.

Beth nodded, smiling in return.

'You speak Spanish?' asked the girl in halting English.

'Yes, I do,' replied Beth in her Spanish that now, thanks to Rosita, was accentless and fluent.

'I'm Catalina Ruiz, Jacey's nurse during this shift. I'm glad I caught you.'

'Why—what's happened?' demanded Beth, fear leaping in her.

'Nothing—Jacey's fine,' soothed the nurse. 'In fact, he's sleeping at the moment.'

'Sleeping?' echoed Beth, puzzled.

'His tummy's been rather sore this morning, which is only to be expected, so he's been given a sedative.' She gave a sudden grin. 'I nearly forgot—I promised to tell you how brave he was when he had his injection.'

'Oh, dear, an injection,' sighed Beth with a rueful smile, Catalina's relaxed manner reassuring her. 'I'm sure he didn't take too kindly to that.'

'I'm afraid I had to take an oath regarding his initial reaction,' grinned the nurse, 'so my lips are sealed. Would you like me to bring you in a coffee?'

'That's very kind of you,' replied Beth, 'but I shan't have one just now.'

'Perhaps later, then. I'll be popping in and out regularly to check on Jacey.'

Beth smiled her thanks, then entered the room and went to her son's bedside.

'Hello, my darling,' she whispered, her heart full to overflowing. She gave a start of surprise when Jacey's eyes opened. 'Your nurse told me you were asleep!' she exclaimed, bending over and kissing him.

'Catalina?' he queried, reaching up a chubby hand to stroke her face.

'Yes, Catalina,' murmured Beth. 'And she told me how brave you were when you had an injection.'

'It was a horrible 'jection,' he complained sleepily, 'but my tummy only hurts a little bit now... Where's Yaya?'

'She'll be coming later,' replied Beth, her love for him an exquisitely sharp pain within her. 'She had to go home last night and—'

'But didn't you go home with her, Mamá?' exclaimed Jacey, plainly puzzled.

Beth shook her head. 'I'm sure Yaya must think I'm a silly-billy, but I wanted to stay here in Palma to be near to you.'

'You're not really a silly-billy,' he protested loyally, his eyelids beginning to droop with sleep. 'And Yaya couldn't stay with you because she has to go to the gallery... When I'm big and do beautiful paintings, Yaya's going to put them in her gallery—won't that be nice?'

'That will be lovely,' she whispered softly. Conscious of the battle he was having to keep his eyes open, she drew the chair beside her close to the bed. 'I'm afraid I'm feeling a bit tired, so do you mind if I put my head down beside yours?'

He gave a sigh of contentment, clumsily wrapping an arm around her head as Beth laid it on the pillow next to his, and was asleep almost the instant he had completed the action. It was only when she was sure he was fully asleep that she extricated her head and rose. Now there was no thought in her mind of specific words as she slipped from the room, just the knowledge that she had a task to fulfil with whatever words came to her.

She went over to the reception area where one of the nurses was filling in a chart. 'I need to have a word with Dr Caballeros,' she told her. 'I was wondering if—'

'You're in luck,' the girl smilingly interrupted her. 'Here he is now.'

Beth spun round just as the doors swung closed behind Jaime. Her heart pounding, she almost ran over to him. 'Jaime, I *have* to speak to you!'

'Speak away,' he said, striding past her towards the door of Jacey's room. 'I have your son's notes here,' he added, opening up the folder he was carrying, 'but I haven't had a chance to look through them yet.' Coming to a halt at the door, he glanced down at the top page of the folder, then froze, his eyes widening in disbelief. 'Jaime Carlos?' he queried bemusedly. 'I had no idea you were so taken with my name!'

'Jaime—stop!' she pleaded distractedly as he made to push open the door.

'Beth, what is it?' he demanded, turning to her, a succession of expressions chasing across his face.

'There's no easy way of telling you this!' she exclaimed, her mouth so dry she could barely get the words out. 'Which is why I've found it so… Jaime, he's yours… Jacey is your son.'

'Jaime Carlos,' he muttered hoarsely, taking a reflex step back from her and hitting the door as the colour drained from his face. '*My* son?'

'Jaime, I tried to…' Her words dried up as he swung round and almost hurled himself through the door.

Her heart racing as though it would burst, Beth followed after him, the mother in her prepared to do battle to the death rather than risk her child witnessing the fury of his rejection. But the scene that greeted her froze her to stillness.

Jaime was standing at the foot of the bed, a deathly pallor on his face as he drank in the features of the sleeping child, his knuckles gleaming white against the bedrail his hands fiercely gripped.

In that frozen moment Beth knew without any shred of doubt that he was seeing Jacey as his son, recognizing him as such without question. Thrown though she was by the spontaneous totality of his acceptance, what she found deeply disturbing was the state of complete shock he seemed to be in. His breath was coming in tortured gasps as though he had been on a long, gruelling run.

'Jaime.' Beth spoke his name softly in an attempt to bring him out of his trance-like state. Up until a few seconds ago he hadn't had the slightest doubt who Jacey's father was… And now this. She couldn't make any sense of it. 'Jaime,' she repeated, her tone now pleading.

It was Catalina entering the room that momentarily broke his trance. 'Not now, Nurse,' he muttered hoarsely.

'Is everything all right, Doctor?' Catalina asked, plainly alarmed.

'Everything's fine,' said Beth hastily when Jaime

failed to respond. 'We'll call for you later.' She moved to the head of the bed. 'Jaime, are you all right?'

He looked up from the sleeping child, dragging distracted fingers through his hair before walking round to stand beside her, his eyes filled with an agonized mixture of bewilderment and pain.

Without any consciousness of what she was doing, Beth moved the chair aside to accommodate him. But she was conscious of the sudden sting of tears in her eyes as she watched him sit down on the bed and lower his head to that of his son.

For an instant his face hovered above the upturned one of the sleeping child, drinking in every inch of the features that were a miniature replica of his own. Then he lowered his head further and brushed his lips across those in which the sensual strength of his own had already begun to take shape. With that movement a lock of his hair fell forward onto that of the child and there was no telling one raven strand from the other.

Jacey stirred, opening his eyes and gazing up into the face of his father, a glimmer of a smile touching his lips.

'*Hola*,' he greeted him croakily.

'*Hola*, Jaime Carlos,' murmured Jaime. 'Is your tummy hurting quite a lot again?'

The child nodded, wincing slightly as he did so. 'How did you know?'

'Because I'm a doctor,' replied Jaime gently. 'Your tummy hurts because all that good stuff in the injection you had earlier has been used up by your body.'

Jacey's eyes flew to Beth. 'Mamá, I didn't cry when I had the 'jection—Catalina told you, didn't she?' he exclaimed apprehensively before returning his attention to his father. 'Anyway, my tummy's beginning to feel better now, so I won't have to have another one.'

'You don't have to have another injection,' Jaime reassured him. 'I have another way of getting more of that good stuff into you—one that doesn't hurt.' He reached up and rang the bell over the bed, then smoothed the child's hair back from his forehead, his hand remaining there as he turned when Catalina entered and gave her instructions. 'But there's one thing I want you to promise me,' he told Jacey, once the nurse had left, 'and that is that you won't tell any more fibs about your tummy not hurting... If you promise me that, then I'll explain all about what's making you feel so sore and sick, and how we're going to make it better.'

His eyes wide with trust, Jacey gave his solemn vow not to tell any more fibs, after which his father began fulfilling his part of the bargain. He began with the pain-killing suppository he proposed giving and chuckled at Jacey's none too enthusiastic response.

'I promise you'll hardly even notice me putting it in,' coaxed Jaime, 'and it's much better than an injection.'

The mere mention of an injection converted Jacey instantly. 'Will I be all better after it?' he asked with an innocent optimism that pierced Beth's heart.

Jaime shook his head. 'No, I'm afraid you won't,' he told him candidly, then, in a soft, almost hypnotic voice, began explaining the function of the appendix and how it sometimes went wrong.

The more detail he went into, the more often Beth's anxious eyes flew to her son's face. Each time she looked she saw huge eyes in a trusting little face, hanging on with no trace of alarm to every word being uttered. And when Catalina returned and handed Jaime a covered enamelled dish Jacey endured the indignity of the insertion of the suppository without a murmur.

'See, it really didn't hurt, Mamá,' he reassured her, stretching out his hand for her to hold almost as though sensing she might be feeling left out.

It was when Jaime got to the subject of the actual removal of the appendix that an involuntary gasp of protest escaped her.

'It's all right, Mamá,' Jacey murmured drowsily, giving her hand a reassuring squeeze. 'Jorge had his appendix out and he's got it in a jar.' His eyes moved back to Jaime. 'Can I have mine in a jar?'

'I'm sure that can be arranged,' chuckled Jaime. 'But now I think it's time your *mamá* and I left you to get some more sleep.'

'Will you and Mamá be here when I wake up?' demanded Jacey, his eyes fluttering, then closing.

'Yes,' whispered Jaime, 'we'll be here, little one.' He straightened and removed the rubber gloves he had used to insert the suppository, his hands visibly shaking as he passed the dish holding them to the nurse. Then he picked up the folder lying open on the bed and glanced through it. 'I'll have a look at this later,' he said, handing it to Catalina. 'Please have it sent to my office.' For several seconds he remained seated on the bed, his eyes never leaving the small face until he had satisfied himself his son was soundly asleep.

Then he rose, his face drawn and grim. 'Come, Beth, we must talk—away from all this.'

He took her by the arm and marched her out of the

building without uttering a word. Still with her arm trapped in his grasp, he led her from the clinic grounds, across the road and down a narrow side street to a small bar—one less crammed with boisterous holidaymakers than the couple he had swept her past on the main street.

Having ordered coffee without stopping to consult her, he faced her across the table in a small alcove, his eyes glittering with a confusion of emotions.

'Why, Beth?' he demanded hoarsely. 'How could you do this to me? How could you leave me for so long in such complete ignorance?'

Beth's eyes were glacial as they watched him. He honestly meant it, she thought incredulously. 'How could *I* let *you,* Jaime?' she queried icily. 'When you learned I had a five-year-old son you were only too happy to assume his father was Francisco Suarez. You never for one—'

'Happy?' he broke in angrily. 'Damn it, Beth, given that I'd been told his grandmother was with him, and once I knew his age, what else could I think? You seem to forget that I knew you had been orphaned as a child and would naturally assume any grandmother to be—'

'But you recognized Rosita when you met her,' she cut through his protests accusingly, 'and you knew she couldn't possibly be a blood relative.'

'For God's sake, Beth, by then you'd had plenty of opportunity to tell me, so the thought didn't even cross my mind.' He scowled at her across the table. 'Who knows? Had I known his age when I first saw you yesterday and had I not been told about the grandmother, perhaps then it might have crossed my mind... For God's sake, it's not as though we ever took the sort of risks that would make me think along such lines.' The anger on his face was replaced by a look of dazed introspection. 'What made you change your mind and tell me?' he asked hoarsely. 'The fact that you realized I was bound to find out anyway?'

'It was always my intention to tell you!' she exclaimed, unable to understand her nervous apprehension when she should be feeling relieved over his positive reaction to Jacey. 'I was going to tell you last night, but you were called to the clinic.' She shifted uneasily on her chair. 'If you must know,' she blurted out, 'I found it difficult telling you because I had no idea how you'd react.'

'You were afraid I'd respond negatively to hearing I had a son?' he asked in shocked tones.

'Well, let's face it, ''negative'' would be a pretty mild description of your feelings towards me,' she retorted angrily. 'So how was I to know you wouldn't feel the same towards my son?'

'Because he's my son too, damn it!' he snapped, making no attempt to deny her statement about his feelings about her.

'I'm surprised you actually believed me,' she flung back at him. 'I'm surprised you didn't demand a blood test or something before taking *my* word!'

'What would you have to gain by lying over something like that?' he demanded harshly, then gave a weary shake of his head. 'Beth, have you no idea what I'm feeling? What it is to discover that for all these years there has been a life, a part of me, that I never knew existed?'

Beth felt something harden within her. 'Tell me, Jaime, what is it, exactly, that you feel?' she demanded pitilessly. 'Love? You don't know my son.

Remorse, perhaps? Why should you feel remorse? All that's happened is that nature has taken its time-honoured course—the man having his pleasure and the woman being left to pick up the pieces.' She glanced down at her hands and was puzzled to find them shaking, despite the fact that she felt peculiarly calm. She clasped them tightly together, then continued. 'Or is it the fact that my son happens to have Caballeros blood in his veins—the glorious Caballeros genes in his make-up? Is that your problem, Jaime?' She stopped, despite the part of her that was desperate to continue, halted by fear that the bitterness that had tormented her over the years would now demand its own voice.

'You speak as though I'd been offered a choice and rejected it,' he whispered dazedly. 'Beth, you gave me no choice—you denied me all knowledge of our child.'

Beth hesitated, consciously having to fight off the effects of the stark pain colouring his words.

'And you, no doubt, would have done the honourable thing—dishonourably ditching the fiancée you'd been cheating on—and married me,' she observed caustically.

'Beth, we'd have worked something—'

'Oh, I'm sure you'd have behaved with stunning nobility.' She cut him short, a brittle laugh bursting from her as she fought for control. Then she was seeing his face as it had once been, softened by the warmth of what she had believed was love, and the bitterness broke free. His rejection had been like a dagger plunged deep into her heart, and now she had her own dagger to wield as she chose. 'But you're right, Jaime—you had no choice. You hadn't then and you haven't now—because Jacey is mine and mine alone. Whatever feelings you may imagine you have for him, you can forget them because you are nothing in his life. That's all you ever have been and all you ever will be—nothing!'

'Why did you give him my name?' he demanded hoarsely, his face ghostly pale. 'Why have you brought him up as the Spaniard he undoubtedly is? Why, Beth, if his father is nothing in his life?'

'Why should that be because of you?' she protested agitatedly, feeling suddenly trapped and threatened. 'Can't you understand what Rosita has come to mean to me—that I love her as I would my own mother? My decision to make Mallorca my home was because it's *her* home!' The look in Jaime's eyes only confirmed that her impassioned outburst had had little if any bearing on the questions he had demanded of her.

Her reasons for ensuring that Jacey grew up to be as Spanish as he was English stemmed from her belief in his inalienable right to participate fully in both cultures. Whether or not Jacey ever came to learn of his father, she could never have denied him his Spanish ancestry... She could never have allowed him to grow up a stranger in his father's land.

'I understand and respect how special your love for her is,' stated Jaime quietly. 'But that doesn't tell me why you chose to give our son my name and chose—and I believe more consciously than you're prepared to admit—to raise him as a Spaniard.'

What started as a noncommittal shrug ended up as a weary gesture of resignation, the need for vengeance dying as the last of her energy seeped from her.

'I can't deny that the memory of the harshness of much of my own childhood made me want to give

Jacey the best I possibly could,' she conceded tonelessly. 'Perhaps because I was so conscious of what I had been denied, there was no way I could deny Jacey his Spanish heritage… It would have been like denying half of Jacey himself.'

'I haven't forgotten what you told me of your childhood and I thank you for giving so much to…Jacey.' He had hesitated slightly before speaking the name. 'God, Beth, you were so poor,' he exploded suddenly. 'Why couldn't you bring yourself to let me know…? How, for God's sake, did you survive?'

'Does it really matter, Jaime?' she protested wearily, his reference to her poverty bringing back her own thoughts of his background and her own ignorance, at nineteen, of the often rigid barriers of class. Was that all it had been, she wondered with a sudden stab of sadness—a matter of class? She had been so convinced he loved her when he had left to spend a few days with his father in Barcelona. Yet it was during his stay there that he had met up again with the girl he had never mentioned to her; and it was that other girl he had asked to be his wife. Had those few days among his own circle opened his eyes to her unsuitability as anything other than a holiday fling? Or had she simply mistaken for love the lust that had led him to betray the girl he had loved all along? 'It was all so long ago,' she muttered, half to herself—and anyway, what did it matter now? 'The only thing that matters now is Jacey and his well-being.'

'There we're in total agreement, Beth,' he stated huskily. 'He's all that matters.'

Beth was conscious of innumerable unasked questions hovering between them as they returned to the clinic, but also of a sense of truce. It was the intensity of her love for her son that tempered her disquiet at recognizing an element of ambivalence in her attitude towards Jaime. It was only right that bitterness and hatred should take second place to their concern over Jacey, she told herself firmly—a concern she knew unquestionably to be shared.

'I'm operating this afternoon,' he told her, uncertainty softening the remoteness of his features as he turned to her at the door of Jacey's room. 'I'll see you when I've finished… But would you mind if I looked in on him now? I did promise to be there when he awoke.'

'Jaime, you don't have to ask,' Beth heard herself protest unsteadily as the stark pleading in his eyes melted something deep within her.

By the time Rosita arrived, less than half an hour after Jaime had left, Beth was feeling strung out and close to tears.

Jacey had fought sleep for almost twenty minutes after Jaime's departure and had worked himself into a state of fretful anxiety. Querulously rejecting the attempts of both Beth and the nurse to answer the questions he would intermittently spring on them, he had kept asking for Jaime.

Flinging herself into the older woman's arms, Beth gave her a barely coherent account of all that had happened and the state Jacey had managed to get himself into until sleep had finally overcome him.

'Jaime shouldn't have been so explicit with him,'

she protested as Rosita released her from a comforting hug and sat down on the chair Catalina had produced before leaving. 'He told him all the gory details about removing the appendix and now Jacey keeps coming up with questions... He's not interested in what Catalina or I have to say—it's only Jaime he wants.'

'Is it Jaime the father or Jaime the doctor he wants?' asked Rosita quietly.

Beth stiffened, shaking her head vehemently. 'He doesn't know anything,' she replied tensely, 'so of course it's the doctor.'

'Yet you already feel threatened, my love?'

'I—I know it's stupid, but...' She shut her eyes tightly, picturing how glamorous the tall, good-looking surgeon must appear to an impressionable five-year-old. 'Perhaps I'm wrong to criticize Jaime for telling him so much,' she sighed, 'because I know, in my heart of hearts, that it reassured him, despite the state he got himself into just now... He even has plans to keep his appendix in a jar, just like Jorge—'

'Yaya,' murmured Jacey, his eyes fluttering open. 'Were you lonely last night without Mamá and me?'

'A little bit,' chuckled Rosita, leaning over and kissing him.

He wrapped his arms round her neck and gave her a hug. 'Don't worry, you won't be lonely for long because tomorrow I'm going to have an operation— my big doctor told me all about it—and then we'll soon all be home.' He studied Rosita carefully to see how she was taking the news.

'What, an operation like the one Jorge had when he was in Madrid?' asked Rosita, suitably awed.

He nodded solemnly. 'But I won't be able to come home right away after, because my tummy will be very sore for a while and I'll have stitches.'

'And then you'll be completely better,' said Rosita softly. 'You know, if ever I got sick I think I'd want to come to this hospital to be made better.'

The three of them chatted for over an hour and Jacey was at his sweetest and most loving, until he became tired and tried to fight it.

Rosita glanced at her watch. 'Is it really that time?' she exclaimed brightly. 'I forgot to tell Mamá that I have an important meeting to go to soon.'

'Is it very important?' demanded Jacey, petulance creeping into his tone.

'I'm afraid it is,' sighed Rosita. 'But it's just as well I have to go now; I can see how tired you are.'

'But you didn't meet my big doctor,' he protested tearfully. 'When's he coming back, Mamá?'

'As soon as he's finished what he's doing,' soothed Beth, reaching over and stroking his head. 'He promised you he would... And Catalina and I have made a list of all the things you want to ask him.' He was calling for his father, she thought numbly, and it was affecting her almost like a rejection. 'You snuggle up while I see Yaya to her car.'

'We might as well be honest,' murmured Rosita, once they had left the room. 'He's never in the best of moods when he's tired and determined not to go to sleep. And the fact that he's been sedated is plainly making it that much worse.' She reached up and gently pinched Beth's cheek. 'And try to stop reading too much into his calling for Jaime. He's a bright little boy and knows perfectly well he can get far more information out of a doctor than he can from us.'

'I know,' sighed Beth, giving her a spontaneous hug. 'Did you mean it about having a meeting, or was that just a ploy to get Jacey to rest?'

'A bit of both,' smiled Rosita. 'I put off someone who was coming up to the gallery tomorrow. He gave me his address here in Palma and suggested I drop in if I had the time, but it was left very open.'

'I hate to think of you putting off business appointments to—'

'Beth,' interrupted the older woman, her tone chiding. She linked her arm through Beth's. 'I'm off to see him now, so where's the problem? And while you walk me to my car I can nag you about how tired you look.' She glanced up at Beth as they walked along, her expression anxious. 'Darling, I know that it can't be easy for you staying at Jaime's place, but—'

'But the pros outweigh the cons,' Beth finished for her with a wan grin. 'With tomorrow looming up, even I can see that.' She gave a small shudder. 'Though, to be honest, I'm trying my best not to dwell on thoughts of tomorrow—as I'm sure you are, too.'

Rosita nodded grimly. 'I had thought of coming down early, to see our little man before they operate,' she said. 'But you know what I'm like when I've something on my mind—so perhaps I'll just give the gallery office a good sort out, instead of driving us both mad here.'

Beth was laughing as they approached the car. 'God help that poor office. I don't think I'll ever forget the going over you gave those dreadful digs I was in when I went into the first stages of labour,' she chuck-led. 'I doubt if the students next door will either—they were convinced I'd suddenly decided on a home delivery and that you were trying to sterilize the place!' She was still smiling, but tears filled her eyes as she gave the Spanish woman a fierce hug. 'God was very good to me letting me find you,' she whispered in a choked voice.

'And equally good to me, my darling,' replied Rosita, her voice unsteady. 'And I'm so proud of the way you're coping...with all of this.'

CHAPTER FOUR

DARKNESS had long since fallen when Jaime returned and once more Beth was conscious of the increasing ambivalence of her feelings towards him. Still clad in the lightweight clothing of the operating theatre, he looked suddenly much younger than his thirty-two years and there was a vulnerable look about him so reminiscent of Jacey that her fingers itched to soothe it away.

'I'm much later than I thought I'd be,' he apologized, his words uncharacteristically hesitant.

'You look tired!' exclaimed Beth, the words out before she was aware of them forming.

'Do I?' he asked, his eyes locking with hers as he walked to the foot of Jacey's bed. 'It's been a long day.' The ease of his words belied the conflicting emotions smouldering in the dark depths of the eyes still locked with hers.

'Yes, I suppose it has,' muttered Beth, rising to her feet as she tore herself free from his mesmerizing gaze. 'I—I think I'll give my legs a bit of a stretch,' she stammered, experiencing an almost overwhelming urge to run. She turned when she reached the door. 'He's been asking for you,' she told him quietly, and felt fear stab through her at the sight of the wonderment her words brought to his face.

First her inability to interpret what she had seen in his eyes had made her want to flee, she thought wretchedly, then she was terrified by what needed no interpreting whatever... Much more of this and she would end up a mental wreck.

Perhaps Rosita was right about the lack of wisdom in closing her mind to all thought of him for all these years... It had allowed her to forget the totality with which she had loved every aspect of him, and now she was paying the price of remembering. Changed though he undoubtedly was mentally, physically he was still very much the man she had once loved so passionately, she thought with an edgy, wary caution as she walked through to the back of the building... And now there was no way she could obliterate the memories.

She stepped outside to where darkness had drained the fierceness of the heat from the day, leaving the air gentle, almost cooling, against her skin. Looking around her, she found, in complete contrast to the crisp, well-tended lawns lying to the front, a small copse of cypress trees. She could bring Jacey here when he was up and about, she told herself, imagining the long, protective shadows the tall, stately trees would provide against the heat of the day.

She came to an open space amid the solitude of the cypresses and paused by a stone birdbath at its centre. She gazed around her, the peacefulness of her surroundings serving only to accentuate the chaos within her.

It didn't take a genius to work out that her preoccupation with Jacey's sudden illness made coping with Jaime's reappearance in her life much more difficult. Except that she was barely coping at all, she reminded herself wearily. Her thoughts seemed to have developed a will of their own, not simply filling her mind with memories of loving Jaime but hurtling her back in time and frequently rendering the past indistinguishable from the present.

Her body was just as difficult to control, every now and then devastating her with blasts of naked sexual longing that left her shaken and appalled. Devastating, yes—but perhaps not inexplicable, she reasoned cautiously with herself. Even in her total innocence she had recognized their explosive sexual compatibility as something very much out of the ordinary. And because there had been no one since him it was probably only natural for her body to respond as it was doing after the shock of again meeting the man responsible for so powerful an awakening.

And what about those other women? she wondered, hugging her arms around her as though to ward off coldness as memories of what Rosita had told her returned... Those women he had turned to in the desolation of his grief; were there some whose bodies still tortured *them* with memories of passion?

She gave an exasperated shake of her head. She had managed to string together a few coherent thoughts, she remonstrated impatiently with herself, so why spoil it? Neither those unfortunate women nor the terrible reason for their existence were subjects she could afford to dwell on. As she tried to blank out such thoughts a picture of Jaime and Jacey leapt to her mind, the two faces suddenly merging into one, and a grim tension crept over her features. She turned and, with a deeply troubled heart, slowly retraced her steps.

Earlier the evening shift nurse had now and then popped in and chatted to her while Jacey had slept and, as she opened the door, Beth was hoping the girl had returned.

But there was no nurse; just Jacey, one small hand

raised to stroke the face of the man now at his bedside, and Jaime, his face glistening with tears.

'Why are you so sad?' whispered the child.

'Because I love you and I can't bear to see you
hurting.'

'Why do you love me so much?' asked Jacey, and
the man raised his tear-stained face and turned to
Beth, his eyes pleading.

Beth nodded, an instinctive nod; yet, even as she
did so, something deep within her cried out in protest,
filling her with a deep, intangible fear.

'I love you more than you could ever imagine…because I am your father, Jaime Carlos.'

'I knew you'd come,' breathed Jacey contentedly,
motioning Beth over to the bed. 'I made a wish when
I blew out my birthday candles that my *papá* would
come.'

It was something he had never spoken of to her, a
secret dream locked away in his heart, only to be revealed when it at last came true… The realization
brought a choked sob to Beth's lips as tears streamed
down her cheeks.

Blindly she stumbled to the bed, her fingers reaching out to clasp Jacey's outstretched hand.

'Don't cry, Mamá,' he reproached her sleepily.
'Papá will take care of you.' His eyes were drooping
as he returned his attention to his father. 'Usually
Mamá's very brave; you ask Yaya. Even when she
cut her finger once, she didn't cry.'

Beth felt as though a dam had burst in her and
helplessly clamped her free hand over her mouth to
stifle the sobs over which she had no control.

'It's all right, Beth, you can cry all you need… He's
asleep.'

She felt Jaime's arms encircle her, rocking her gently, but there was nothing anyone could do to silence the sobs shuddering through her.

'I've rung for the nurse,' he told her gently. 'She'll be here any moment now and I'll take you home.'

Even on the journey back to the house the tears barely subsided, choking out of her with an abandon that made her fear she was in the throes of some sort of minor breakdown.

With his arm supporting her and her head buried against him, Jaime led her into the house, then seated her on a stool in the clinical white kitchen.

Beth screwed up her eyes against the glaring brightness of the lights, her mind reeling even as her sobs subsided to no more than the random hiccup.

'Well, you obviously needed a good cry,' said Jaime. He stooped towards her and produced a handkerchief with which he lightly wiped the residual tears from her face.

'I—I suppose it's the idea of what Jacey has to face tomorrow,' Beth stammered. But she wasn't in the least sure. She knew what had triggered her tears, but couldn't fathom what had caused them to overwhelm her. 'Jaime—why are you looking at me like that?' she demanded as she turned and found him staring at her as though he had had a shock. 'What's wrong?'

'I… It's only just now occurred to me that we're speaking in Spanish,' he muttered dazedly. 'You're fluent… And your accent has completely disappeared.'

Beth was disconcerted to feel her cheeks colouring with pleasure. 'That's down to Rosita,' she told him.

'Well, she's done a magnificent job. I—' He broke off, frowning in puzzlement. 'Is Señora Rubio by any chance the woman you spent so much time with on your first time in Mallorca—the one you said worked in an art gallery and used to help you with your Spanish?'

Beth nodded, wondering why something in her froze whenever he made any reference to the past. 'Obviously I'd no idea then who she was, let alone that she owned the gallery.'

'No—you wouldn't have,' he stated abruptly. 'It's nice that Jacey calls her Yaya,' he added, clumsily switching the subject he now seemed no more comfortable with than she was. 'It's a Mallorcan term for grandmother.'

'I know it is,' Beth responded stiltedly. 'She told me of it the day Jacey was born…the day I asked her to be his grandmother.'

'It's right that you did… You look exhausted, Beth,' he muttered, again suddenly changing the subject. 'You need to sleep properly tonight—I'll get you something.'

Before she could say anything, he had disappeared from the room.

He reappeared a few seconds later and handed her a glass. 'Don't worry, I'm not trying to poison you,' he informed her drily when she hesitantly took the glass from him. 'It's a herbal relaxant they sometimes use on the paediatric wards for children who get unduly stressed.'

It was on the tip of Beth's tongue to tell him that it would take more than a few herbs to stop her getting stressed around him, but she drank the slightly acidic potion instead, then bade him goodnight and went to her room.

The way she had gone to pieces preyed on her

while she bathed. At the back of her mind was the certainty that it went far deeper than she was fully conscious of: she could actually feel it, whatever it was, hovering elusively somewhere in the furthest regions of her mind, refusing to be pinned down.

She was still trying to pin it down over an hour later as she tossed and turned in her bed, battling against both the herbal concoction and the sheer exhaustion threatening to overcome her.

In a drowsy effort to discipline a mind begging for sleep, she retraced the events of the day step by step. A few minutes later she sat bolt upright in the bed.

Moments before she had been reduced to tears, she had been assailed by an inexplicable sense of fear... Was it unconsciously triggered by the tears on Jaime's face as he had gazed down at Jacey? Tears of despair brought on by something about Jacey's condition that he couldn't bring himself to tell her?

She pressed her hands to her face, scarcely able to breathe as everything fell into place. When she had mentioned tomorrow's operation, he had made no attempt to reassure her, but instead had side-stepped her words, distracting her by claiming only then to have noticed her fluency in Spanish and then, just to make sure she remained distracted, by drugging her up to the eyeballs!

She leapt from the bed and raced down the stairs. Too confused by panic, she didn't stop to question why Jaime should still be sitting where she had left him in the kitchen. It was the cognac bottle and the large measure in the glass beside him on the table that struck stark terror in her.

Jaime rarely drank; that was one of the safer memories she had of him and something she was convinced would not have changed. Then she saw the dark shadow of beard against the smoothness of his face, but most of all she saw the unmistakable despair in the eyes that rose to hers. The memory of the conflicting emotions she had seen in his eyes and had fled from so much earlier that evening now merely confirmed her every fear.

Barely conscious of what she was doing, Beth strode over, picked up the glass and drained its contents in one go.

'Are you out of your mind?' exploded Jaime, gazing in angry disbelief at the now empty glass he had snatched from her.

'If I hadn't drunk it you would have!' she flung at him agitatedly. 'And the last thing I want is you drunk—I need you to be coherent so that—'

'*Me* drunk—incoherent?' he demanded icily, slamming the glass down onto the table. 'I'd say that's a pretty fair description of the state you'll be in once that slug of cognac's taken effect. I'd have hoped you'd have more sense than to mix a sedative, no matter how mild, with alcohol.'

Beth was momentarily distracted by an awareness of her thoughtless stupidity, but only briefly.

'I trusted you,' she accused him, her voice unnaturally loud in the stillness of the house. 'You're hiding something from me—I know you are!'

He rubbed his hands wearily down his face. 'I'm hiding nothing from you, Beth.' His tone was that of a man exhausted, as were his movements when he rose from the stool and walked past her, out of the room.

'Oh, aren't you?' Beth cried, racing after him. 'You can't even bring yourself to face me!'

'I can face you, Beth,' he snapped. 'I intend facing you, if only to stop you ranting like this…but I'm dead on my feet.' He marched into the elegant living room and flung himself down on a sofa. 'I was about to fall off that stool. So, tell me what's—'

'Stop changing the subject!' she shrieked, standing over him threateningly.

'For God's sake, Beth, stop shouting at me, will you? I haven't the slightest idea what you're going on about and screaming at me like this isn't going to help my thought processes in the least.'

'You know perfectly well what I mean. Jacey! What's *really* wrong with him?'

'God almighty, Beth—what's wrong with Jacey is that he has appendicitis!'

'But it's not just that,' she cried frantically. 'You're lying! I know you are…I saw you cry.'

'And you've got it into your head that I cried because Jacey's condition is worse than I've admitted to you?' he asked, his voice hoarse with disbelief.

Beth nodded, the feeling of uncertainty now creeping through her unrelated to the sudden spinning of her head.

'Beth, I swear to God—I'll even swear on Jacey's life if you want—that his is nothing more than a mercifully uncomplicated case of appendicitis.' He leaned back and closed his eyes. 'Beth, apart from the fact that you're exhausted both mentally and physically, it's not in the least unusual for mothers of sick children to become irrational at times like this. I'm sorry, so very sorry, that my behaviour was responsible for such an erroneous reaction in you.' He gave a small shudder. 'But how can I expect you to understand why I should behave so uncharacteristically when I can't even understand it myself?' he whispered, almost as though asking himself.

Beth sat down beside him and briefly closed her eyes in an attempt to clear the woozy spinning of her head.

'I want to understand, Jaime,' she pleaded brokenly. 'I just couldn't understand why I'd gone to pieces like that. Of course, deep down, I'm terrified out of my wits by the very idea of Jacey having an operation tomorrow. But I had it under control, up until then, because I could see how irrational it was... Then, a few moments ago, when I remembered how you'd cried...'

'Your deduction was wrong, I swear to—'

'I believe you, Jaime,' she cut in unsteadily. 'I honestly do now.'

He made as though to speak, then gave an angry shake of his head before making a concerted effort to pull himself together. 'You gave birth to Jacey; since his very beginning he's been part of you, of your life... Yet I learned of his existence through little more than chance.'

'And you never for an instant queried that he was yours,' muttered Beth, remembering her fears that he would.

He shrugged. 'No, but even if I had, once I saw his blood group I'd have known.'

The look Beth gave him was puzzled and questioning.

'I have an unusual blood group,' he stated in a peculiarly toneless voice. 'Not worryingly so, but rare enough for it to be too much of a coincidence that Jacey should also have it.'

'Oh, I see,' muttered Beth vaguely, remembering

him reading Jacey's full name from the chart he had been holding when she had broken the news to him, and wondering when he had actually got around to checking the blood group.

'Perhaps you do. But what I don't see is how you could have been so certain... I mean, certain enough to give him my name.'

Beth felt a sickening sensation stir in the pit of her stomach. 'He has that same triangular birthmark on his left shoulder that you have on yours,' she heard herself reply, and wondered why on earth she hadn't simply come out with the truth.

'There are so many things I don't know about him.' He tilted his head back against the sofa, his eyes closed. 'And it's only now that I'm beginning to see how many things there are that have scarcely touched my life. I've seen mothers weep for their sick children and accepted it as only normal. But how many times have I seen fathers weep? I cannot say, because I've always turned away from the men, knowing that even in the most tragic of circumstances they wouldn't wish another man to witness their...weakness.'

'Weakness?' echoed Beth, aghast. 'Jaime, you're so wrong. Where someone he loves is concerned, no true man would give a damn about his *macho* image!'

'You claim that I can't love Jacey,' he accused her, ignoring her protest, 'that my feelings are no more than a primitive genetic response... Perhaps you're right,' he conceded hopelessly, 'but nothing you or anyone else can say can alter what I'm feeling.' He straightened suddenly, an agony of anger and pleading in his eyes as they searched her face. 'The last time I cried freely was when I was fourteen years old and my mother died... I have been reduced to tears by

grief since. But even when my father—' He broke off
with an angry shake of his head.

'Your father?' coaxed Beth softly, her mind balking
from any thought of the tears he must have shed for
the woman he had intended marrying.

'No, I can't... I don't wish to talk about my father... Not now.' He frowned, again shaking his head.
'You say there is no weakness, no shame—but there
is, Beth. I can't stop myself feeling less of a man for
the tears I shed today; for the tears that are within me
now.' He slumped back against the sofa, his eyes closing once more. 'What is it I feel for that little boy,
Beth?' he begged hoarsely. 'If it isn't love, then
there's an emotion far stronger than love. You speak
of irrational fears and I understand you. The doctor I
am has the knowledge that proves how utterly irrational those fears actually are... But it doesn't stop
them haunting the father I've suddenly found myself
to be.'

'I was wrong, Jaime, and I'm sorry,' whispered
Beth, her mind fighting her body's strident cry for
sleep as it pitied him his inhibiting, peculiarly masculine attitude to his own feelings. She knew she
could no longer deny him those feelings, nor the unexpected love that had prompted them. 'Perhaps I
can't understand how or why, but I do believe you
love Jacey.'

He opened his eyes and she saw the brightness of
unshed tears glittering in them. It was then that both
her mind and body gave up their futile battle and, with
no true awareness of what she was doing, she opened
her arms to him.

Almost as Jacey might have, he laid his head
against her breast, his shadowed cheek warm and

rasping against the fine lawn of her nightdress. And, as she would have with Jacey, she ran her fingers through his hair, smoothing it gently back from where it fell, rich and black, across his forehead.

'It's you and me and the doctor,' were the words she offered him as sleep began to carry her away, 'and as long as we keep listening to the doctor we'll be all right.'

There was a moment, in the mists of her sleep, when Beth felt cold and tried to draw the covers around her. But in her dream-filled state those covers obligingly nestled themselves around her of their own accord, cocooning her in their protective warmth.

Later, voices entered her dreams—women's voices that were answered by the deep, sleep-slurred rumble of a man. She imagined she heard Rosita's voice and tried to call to her, but then the warmth sheltering her was stripped from her and she whimpered in protest. The voices were still floating around her as she reached out to recapture the warmth. Then she experienced the sensation of being lifted back into the protection of that warmth and she slipped into the depths of a dreamless sleep.

Beth awoke at eight-thirty but, despite a long shower and some strong coffee, served to her by an attentive maid, her mind kept clinging to the vestiges of sleep, shying in horror from the humiliating reality of full awakening.

The trouble was she could remember so little of what had happened, she thought, mortification washing over her in huge waves. She couldn't for the life of her work out the confused reasoning that had led her to down the brandy... Why on earth hadn't she simply thrown it in the sink if she'd been so hell-bent on his not having any more of it? And to do so after having had that sedative—she could have freaked out on such a combination! She shuddered, then took a sip of coffee, wincing with the effort it took simply to raise the cup to her mouth. For all she knew she *had* freaked out, she realized, almost dropping the cup in shock. She could remember as far as Jaime convincing her that there was nothing more than appendicitis wrong with Jacey…but the rest was a complete blank!

She glanced at her watch and leapt to her feet in consternation. In less than an hour Jacey would be having his pre-med!

'Don Jaime left the keys of his car on the hall table for you,' the maid told Beth, arriving with fresh coffee. 'But wouldn't you like some breakfast before you leave?'

Beth shook her head. 'No, thank you—I don't want to be late,' she said with an apologetic smile. 'But how did Don Jaime get to the clinic?'

'Señora Rubio took him,' replied the woman, smiling broadly. 'She said to tell you she couldn't sleep…and also that you should have a good lie in.'

'Well, I've certainly had that,' smiled Beth, albeit drug-and-alcohol induced, she thought with a silent groan of horror. She picked up her cup and finished her coffee, her heart going out to Rosita as she wondered whether she had actually heard her voice, or whether it had been part of her dream.

Having decided to put all thoughts of last night behind her, she even managed a wry smile as she got into Jaime's car and discovered it was an Aston Martin—a far cry from Rosita's little runabout and yet another reminder of the vast difference in their backgrounds. But she gave a tense, angry shrug as she started up the car.

Driving his car, living in his house…she was putting her trust in Jaime again, warned a harsh inner voice, just as she had once before. No! This time it was different. Before he had been a man bent on seduction and in her naivety she had been unable to see that the only prize he had sought was her body. This time she was dealing with a man possessed and humbled by one of the purest of all loves—that of a father for his child.

Oh, Jaime, she thought sadly as she eased the powerful car through the traffic, it's knocked the earth from under you and who knows which of us is the more surprised?

She remembered the anguish she had seen on his face and heard in his voice, and found herself shaking her head to ward off a sudden memory of the rasping warmth of his cheek against her breast, her arms cradling him in comfort… No, that had all been part of her drunken dreaming.

She gave another, more positive shake of her head as she parked the car in a consultant's bay. It was ridiculous thinking of herself as though she'd suddenly turned into a lush, she told herself firmly. She had made a stupid mistake last night, so enough of this making a mountain out of the tiniest of molehills.

She raced in and up to Jacey's room.

'Beth!'

'Mamá!'

She kissed first Rosita, then her pale, though beaming son. 'That Yaya can be very naughty at times,' she sighed as she took the chair next to Rosita's by the bed, shaking her head in mock exasperation. 'She's supposed to be in Pollensa, tidying up the gallery.'

'She's going to go back and tidy it, Mamá,' exclaimed Jacey protectively. 'But she wanted to give me a kiss before I had my operation—didn't you, Yaya?'

Rosita nodded gravely. 'I told you Mamá would think I was naughty,' she told him conspiratorially, 'but it was more than worth it for all those hugs and kisses I've just had.'

Jacey squirmed with delight, then scrutinized his mother's face. 'Papá said you'd be late because he was making you have a very long sleep,' he announced contentedly. 'Did he give you a 'pository?'

'No, darling, he didn't,' murmured Beth, having difficulty biting back her laughter as she drank in every feature of that small face. 'Just something rather nasty to drink—I think I'd even have preferred an injection.'

'It must have been very, very nasty.' He pulled a glum face. 'I have to have an injection today,' he announced with a sigh. '*And* I didn't have any breakfast.'

'I can see we're going to have to feed you up with all your favourite things when we get you home,' chuckled Rosita, rising. 'Now, I'd better be off and get that gallery tidied. Would you mind if Mamá walked me to my car?'

Jacey shook his head and put his arms up to hug her, wincing sharply as he did so.

'Soon that sore tummy of yours will be all better,' Rosita promised him softly, a catch in her voice.

They passed Catalina on their way down the corridor. 'I'm afraid they've had to put Jacey's operation back a couple of hours,' she told them apologetically. 'An emergency appendectomy was brought in a short while ago... Dr Caballeros will have a word with you the moment he's free.'

'I feel sorry for that other poor soul,' sighed Rosita, 'but it's almost a comfort to have such proof that Jacey's case really isn't regarded as in any way urgent.' She turned and looked at Beth, her expression guarded and anxious. 'I asked you to come with me because I needed to speak to you away from those wagging little ears.'

'Of course you did!' exclaimed Beth, and told her everything that had happened between father and son the previous evening. 'Rosita, Jacey didn't bat an eyelid,' she sighed. 'He just nonchalantly informed us that he'd known his father would come, because that had been his birthday wish... He's accepted Jaime as though he's always known him—' She broke off, remembering how she had told Jaime that what he felt for his son couldn't possibly be love. She had said those things before she had witnessed the unquestioning love on Jacey's face; before she had seen the tears of love on Jaime's.

'Rosita, I...I said such cruel things to Jaime... I told him it couldn't possibly be love he felt for Jacey. I should have told him last night that I didn't mean it... Oh, Rosita, you'll never believe what an idiot I made of myself.' She groaned and told her about the sedative and the brandy. 'I can't even remember how I got to bed!' The instant the words were out, her cheeks became crimson.

'It was I who suggested Jaime put you to bed,' stated Rosita quietly, her eyes betraying an inner battle as they scrutinized Beth's face. 'I... You were sound asleep on the living-room sofa when I arrived shortly before six.'

'Just before six!' gasped Beth. 'You poor love, you really couldn't sleep.'

'No,' she agreed almost abruptly, then hesitated, as though searching for words. 'But as for Jaime—I think you can rest assured that he knows you didn't mean what you said, though—' She broke off, biting her lower lip in consternation. 'But it's you I'm worried about, my darling, and the way all this is affecting you.'

'I'll be fine once we've got Jacey safely back home,' said Beth, willing them both to believe it.

'Will you?' asked Rosita sadly, halting by her car as yet another of the worries troubling her came to mind. 'It's bound to come out—the entire hospital must know by now. And it's not just Jacey, though the nurse's eyes nearly popped from her head when he greeted Jaime as ''Papá'' this morning—it's Jaime too. The pair of them are wallowing in their new-found relationship—' She broke off in belated realization that now was not the time for her to be voicing any of her many fears. 'You see how I waffle on when I'm trying to distract myself from what's really on my mind!' she exclaimed, forcing a rueful smile to her unwilling lips. She reached up and hugged Beth tightly. 'You get back to Jacey, while I give that gallery office the going over of its life... And you ring me there, darling, once our little man's out of the theatre.'

'I'll ring you,' promised Beth, hugging her in return. 'And just you drive carefully.'

Beth made her way slowly back to the building,

thoughts scurrying around in the back of her mind that she had no desire to examine. Just as she was entering the paediatric wing, Jaime joined her.

'You look exhausted,' he informed her brusquely.

'That's a fair description of how I feel,' she responded with forced lightness, somewhat thrown by the remark and the fact that it was also a pretty accurate description of the way he looked. 'I still can't believe how stupid I was, downing that brandy after the sedative. It serves me right for ending up feeling as though I'd been up boozing and boogieing for most of the night.'

His eyes widened slightly as they flicked over her face. 'I believe the nurse has already told you that the operation is to be delayed a little... I'm sorry, I really am—it's something we could both do without.'

'I'm just grateful that Jacey isn't that emergency case they rushed in!' exclaimed Beth, glancing at him in puzzlement. He sounded exactly the way she felt—tense and on edge—but it surprised her that she was making a much better job of hiding it than he was. 'Jaime, will you be in there with him—when they operate?' she asked quietly.

He shook his head. 'I don't think an operating theatre is a suitable place for a father,' he replied, 'especially not when that father happens to be a surgeon himself.'

'I suppose not,' Beth murmured, the palpable tension in him threatening her own veneer of control. 'But what do parents do to while away the time when their child is being operated on?' she asked, her voice trembling.

'That's something we're both about to find out,' he

replied, gazing down at her as they approached the door of Jacey's room.

It was the smile he attempted, which failed to come off, that tore through Beth's defences. In a purely spontaneous gesture of understanding, she reached for his hand. He swung round, breaking contact the instant their hands touched, halting so abruptly that she stumbled against him. He took a breath, as though about to speak, then let it whisper from him in silence as their eyes locked. It wasn't the savage wave of desire blasting through her that shook Beth to the core, but the mirror image of that ungovernable desire blazing from the eyes locked with hers. She momentarily closed her eyes, blinded by what she was seeing. When she opened them she found herself looking up into eyes that now burned with a fury of rejection.

He swung round, his back to her as he placed a hand on the door. 'I want you to meet the surgeon and anaesthetist—they're in with Jacey now.' His hand dropped and he turned back to face her, their mutual love of Jacey drawing him back to her despite his obvious horror at what had just happened. 'These two men are the best,' he told her, his eyes chilling in their blankness. 'The very best.'

CHAPTER FIVE

DESPITE what had happened earlier, and with no awareness of who had made the first move, Jaime and Beth were holding hands as they walked beside the trolley taking their son to the operating theatre. Strong, tanned, masculine fingers entwined with smaller, paler ones, imparting and receiving the understanding and acknowledgement that, where their son was concerned, only each could give the other.

When they reached the doors of the theatre complex each stooped to kiss the pallid, sleeping face, then the doors swished closed and they were alone.

'Let's get out of here,' muttered Jaime and, without waiting for Beth's response, her hand still in his, he led her from the building to the cypress copse she had visited briefly the previous evening.

Beth gazed around, the restful tranquillity of the surroundings again contrasting unsettlingly with the stressful chaos into which her life had plummeted. She wanted things back the way they had been, she thought distractedly; she wanted Jacey well, and back home, and Jaime's disruptive presence obliterated from their lives. She choked back a sob as the utter futility of that last wish struck her like a crippling blow.

'Beth, it's OK,' muttered Jaime, placing an arm around her and drawing her against him. 'Don't be afraid to cry.'

But she continued to fight the tears, driven by a

sudden, vivid memory of the fury of his rejection of what had briefly flared between them. Yet now he could hold her like this—with such tender concern.

'I'll be all right in a moment,' she gulped, accepting the handkerchief he produced. But she would never be all right…because now she understood. It was the mother of his child that he now held so gently, not the woman he loathed yet, to his fury, could still lust for.

'Beth, it doesn't matter if you cry,' he protested softly.

'But it does…' She wasn't the two entities into which he had split her, she was simply Beth! 'I have this feeling that if I start I'll never be able to stop… I'm sorry.'

'Sorry?' he asked, looking down at her with a wry tenderness that trapped the breath in her. 'I don't remember you allowing me any apologies when our roles were reversed last night.'

Beth stiffened, drawing away from the circle of his arm. 'I…I'm afraid I'm a bit hazy as to what happened last night!' she exclaimed shakily. 'I can't believe how stupid I was… I rarely drink spirits at the best of times, let alone with a sedative in me.'

'I should have been a bit quicker getting the glass from you,' he said, the glimmer of a smile touching his mouth. 'Though I have to admit I thought you were going to hurl it at me, not drink it.'

The memory of the bitter harshness of the words she had flung at him crowded accusingly into her mind. 'Jaime… Did I get round to telling you that I accept that you really do love Jacey?'

'You did,' he replied, leaning back and closing his eyes against the sun filtering through the trees.

'I'm glad,' she sighed, and let her eyes roam over his face, taking in the dark circles of tiredness around his eyes and the tell-tale signs of tension clenching his jaw.

She found herself wishing she could compartmentalize him as he had her, separate the man who had so callously destroyed her love from the father still stunned by the love he was feeling for his child.

'I could perform an appendectomy practically standing on my head,' he blurted out, 'but suddenly I can't remember a single step of the procedure.' He straightened in a tense, jerky movement. 'God, I shouldn't have said that!' he exclaimed distractedly. 'I don't want you thinking it's any less straightforward than I've explained to you, because it isn't, I promise you.'

'Not from a surgeon's point of view,' said Beth gently, again surprised to find that she was coping with the strain far better than he was. 'But now you're seeing things from a parent's point of view and from that angle nothing's ever straightforward.'

'I feel there's so much catching up I have to do,' he revealed. 'God—I know nothing! I don't even know where he was born!'

'He was born in London,' said Beth, having to suppress a shudder as a picture of the virtual squalor in which she had been reduced to living flitted through her mind. 'I was living there at the time.'

'Was he a good baby—a healthy baby? Does he speak English? When did you decide to live here— does he go to school here?' he chanted, as though a dam had burst in him. 'Beth, there are a million and more questions lining up in my mind to be asked,' he added with a groan.

Beth glanced up at his tense, strained face, understanding his twin needs—to know about Jacey and to distract them both from this nerve-racking period of waiting—but balking from the inevitable pain of the memories his questions would evoke.

'I'm sorry,' he muttered, turning from her. 'You don't feel I have the right to ask.'

'It's not that at all,' she protested. 'It's just that I don't really know where to start.' Nor how much of the truth she was actually prepared to give him, she added silently to herself.

'Start in London,' he urged quietly. 'Did you stay on at university and complete your degree?'

'No. I left university.' He plainly had no idea about morning sickness, she thought wryly—a gross misnomer for what had gripped her day and night for the best part of four months. It was morning sickness that had forced her to relinquish the dream that had cushioned her for so many years. Unable to continue her degree, she had lost not only the scholarship money, but also the roof over her head.

'But you didn't return to your grandfather's house.' His words were a statement containing no question and they surprised her in that they told her he still remembered her halting confidences all those years ago.

'No—that was out of the question.' In fact, the idea of returning to the unchristian bosom of Agnes had never once entered her head.

'But Señora Rubio—you had already become very close to her?' There was a troubled hesitancy in his tone.

'I had become close to her while I was here—and we wrote when I returned to England.' There was a part of him that suspected it had been a difficult time for her and it was almost as though he was asking her to tell him that it wasn't so, she thought with a stab of resentment. But she would give him the reassurance he wanted, if only because her pride would never let her reveal the truth. And the truth was that as the weeks had passed she had slipped deeper and deeper into despondency. By the time Rosita, with whom she had kept up an unconvincingly optimistic correspondence, had arrived in London, she'd been showing what she now realized were symptoms of clinical depression. 'She came over to London a few months after I went back—the Royal Academy was having an exhibition of her late husband's work.' And that had been the excuse that Rosita had pounced on to go and check for herself how her young friend was coping.

'That was the most terrible tragedy imaginable,' sighed Jaime, shaking his head. 'The nation lost one of its most gifted painters—but poor Señora Rubio lost both her husband and their only child... Her whole life in fact.'

Beth nodded. 'Rosita once told me she felt that was part of what initially drew us together—the fact that tragedy had robbed us both of what we loved most in one moment of horror.'

She closed her eyes, remembering the time when it had entered her bruised consciousness that Rosita had become her shield against the harshness of life. Feeling lost and undeserving of such unstinting generosity, she had tentatively asked why.

'Would my Manolita have had to ask me why?' Rosita had countered gently, and Beth had never felt the need to ask again.

Later, on the day that Jacey had been born, she had

given the woman she loved as a mother the greatest gift she could. 'Meet your grandson, Rosita,' she had whispered as she'd placed the tiny bundle in her arms.

'My Manolita never had a grandmother but I was lucky enough to have one.' Tears of joy had sped down Rosita's cheeks and the words with which she had addressed the bundle in her arms had been choked with love. 'She loved me as I shall love you, more than life itself. Yaya—that's what I called her, as we do in Mallorca, and what you shall call me.' Watching and listening, Beth had had the contentment of knowing that she couldn't have worded her introduction better.

'It must have—' Jaime broke off with a muttered oath as his bleeper went off. He reached into his pocket and switched it off and from another produced a mobile phone. 'It won't be about Jacey,' he told her, stabbing out a number. 'But I'd better see what they want.'

Beth felt the panic that had leapt in her subside as it became clear that the reason he had been paged had indeed nothing to do with Jacey.

'There's been an accident on the outskirts of the city,' he told her, slipping the phone back into his pocket. 'There aren't too many details, but a surgeon is needed on the spot. Beth, I'm the only one available from here, but—'

'No buts,' cut in Beth firmly, rising. 'Jacey's in safe hands—and yours are the hands that someone else needs right now.'

'Beth, I hate leaving you now of all times!' he exclaimed hoarsely, his expression troubled. 'I can't even guess as to when I'll be back.'

For a moment Beth felt he was about to add something else, but instead he took one of her hands and lifted it to his mouth, pressing his lips briefly against it before releasing it, then striding away.

Feeling shaky and peculiarly empty, Beth made her way back to Jacey's room and sat down on one of the bedside chairs. She leaned forward and rested her head on one of the pillows on which her son's head had not long ago lain.

She had mistaken the fear churning in her for fear for Jacey, she realized with sudden clarity; yet at the innermost core of her being she had always believed that Jacey would come through this unscathed. No, her fears had never been for Jacey, she thought, her mind filling with her son's beloved face and suffusing her with love. Then his face altered, maturing swiftly into that of his father, and something quietly broke apart in her.

There was nothing in the least ambivalent about her feelings towards Jaime, she accepted defeatedly. The love she had given him with the reckless, unquestioning naivety of a nineteen-year-old had survived the passing of time. She had loved him in the sunlight of innocence and now, even in the darkness of knowledge, she loved him still.

She had never stopped loving him... His betrayal had come without warning and it was as though the warmth of love in his eyes had become the cold, impersonal glance of a stranger in the swiftness of a blink... But neither her mind nor her heart had been able to adjust to that change, remaining forever trapped in the thrall of the joys of a time that no longer existed.

And now, all these years later, she had witnessed both the joy and the agony of love on his face, seen it glisten through tears as he had gazed at their son. Once she had felt secure in the protection of his love…now her son was beginning to feel the same.

She pressed her face against the pillow as the fears of a protective mother began stirring in her. To a child, love was for ever—once given, never to be taken back. She shook her head in desperation, refusing to acknowledge the thought forming in her mind. The love of a man and a woman was a thing apart, laden with the volatile darkness of passion. The love of a man for his child was unequivocal; the shutters of rejection would never close down on Jaime's feelings for Jacey… Never!

'Tell me about my *papá*,' he had demanded groggily, his eyes only for her in those moments before the pre-med had taken effect, despite the fact that it was his father's hand holding his. But he had drifted away with the drug before she had managed a few, tentative words, acutely hampered by Jaime's presence.

Jacey had inexplicably kept his dreams about his father to himself, but now his dreams had come true and soon she would be faced with a barrage of questions. His quick, probing mind would leave nothing unasked—allow no question to remain unanswered.

She could never deny him the knowledge that he had been conceived in love but she wondered if she could ever look into the brown depths of those innocent eyes and deny the love still raging in her. She could tell her son of the undreamed of peace and happiness she had found on her first visit to Mallorca, but could she ever tell him of the desolation that had driven her away—a desolation that had coloured her life ever since?

* * *

But for a chance meeting with one of her Spanish lecturers in a local supermarket, shortly before leaving for Mallorca, she would never have made that first visit to the plush Formentor Heights hotel…never have met Jaime, whose uncle owned it.

And it had been a Dundee cake that had sealed her fate—the cake she had spontaneously offered to deliver in person to the hotel, rather than let the lecturer go to the expense of putting it in the post.

Her intention had been simply to leave the package at the reception desk for Carlos Lopez, the lecturer's nephew. But Jaime and Carlos had walked through the foyer just as she was giving the receptionist the name, and from that moment on her life had been set on its future course.

Carlos had returned home to Madrid two days after Beth first met him. Two days after that, following a night that had deteriorated into mindless, drunken revelry when the cotton wool she and Beth had stuffed into their protesting ears had proved useless, Lily too had returned home. On both occasions it had been Jaime, with Beth at his side, who had driven them to the airport.

She had never mentioned the almost nightly ordeal to Jaime; just being with him had been enough to erase all thought of the hours spent apart. But three nights after Lily's departure, when a drunken, amorous party-goer had burst into her room and aggressively tried to force her into what he termed 'the fun', she had fled the villa in disgust, running barefoot along the deserted beach in an effort to calm her fright.

Coming across Jaime, a solitary, brooding figure silhouetted against the rocks, had been like a miracle.

Even the dimness of the moonlight had been unable to mask the alarm in his eyes as he had taken her, breathless and dishevelled, into his arms. To banish that alarm she had made light of her experience, telling him only that she had fled the noise of the party.

The hotel had been full and she could remember now, as though it had only been seconds ago, how he had hesitated before suggesting she sleep in one of the rooms in the family suite.

'The noise at the villa could go on till dawn,' he had stated. 'As you've probably realized, my uncle's rarely here, so perhaps I should share with one of the staff. I do not wish to…to compromise you, Beth.'

She had been touched beyond words by the old-fashioned word he had mentally searched his near-perfect vocabulary to find, though she had refused his chivalrous suggestion, pointing out that it wasn't as though they would be sharing a room.

But all it had taken had been one innocently careless touch and passion had flamed between them into an all-consuming rage of need, and later there had been a sob of joy on her lips as she had given herself to him body and soul.

From then on they had drowned in one another, the overwhelming intensity of their mutual obsession making spending more than seconds apart all but impossible. The morning they were to be parted, when Jaime was to spend a few days in Barcelona with his father, they had clung together as though their world was disintegrating around them.

Yet even in his absence she had felt cocooned in the miracle of his love, as though the world had become a different, kinder place—where even the constant night-time din at the villa was almost tolerable.

Even June, Lily's old schoolfriend, had seemed more friendly, accompanying her to the hotel on the first day of Jaime's absence. They had arranged that Beth would receive his calls there as there was no phone at the villa. She had soon discovered the ulterior motive behind June's apparent friendliness—her avid interest in Francisco Suarez, a handsome young economics student who had a summer job as a barman at the hotel—an interest the young man patently did not return.

Beth sat up and leaned back in the chair, hugging the pillow to her. There had been an unusual amount of festivity in the bar when she had arrived there on the third night of Jaime's absence, with everyone drinking champagne. At June's request she had spoken briefly to Cisco before going through to the patio to await Jaime's call. Her thoughts, as always, had centred on Jaime. He had sounded strained and unhappy during his call the previous evening, worried about the timing of his next call.

'I was stupid,' he had fretted. 'I should have arranged for you to have a mobile phone. My father and I have been invited to have dinner with our neighbours tomorrow and I'm not sure what time I'll be able to ring you.'

She had laughed his worries aside, telling him she would gladly wait for ever for his call. In retrospect, it had been a conversation loaded with warning signs, she reflected bitterly, and she had been blind to every one of them. Just as she had been too blind to question Cisco's inordinate discomfiture when she had spoken to him at the bar. At June's behest she had invited him to a party at the villa that night, knowing full well that this was not the first of such invitations and that it would be turned down as all the others had been. It was this inevitable refusal to which she had attributed his obvious unease.

Then one of the waiters had brought her a glass of champagne. 'With the compliments of the proprietor,' he had announced. Even after all those years, Beth still cringed at the memory of her fleeting moment of confused pleasure. She had never actually seen, let alone met, Jaime's elusive uncle Filipe, a man who seemed only to make brief, sporadic visits to the luxury hotel he owned. For that one, fleeting moment she had wondered if Jaime had met up with his uncle, perhaps in Barcelona, and told him about her. Her grossly fanciful thoughts had ended when the waiter had added, almost as an afterthought, 'To celebrate the betrothal of his nephew Don Jaime.'

Even then she had been convinced it was some sort of joke, but the expression on Cisco's face as he appeared on the patio had told her that his intention had been to intercept the waiter and her world had begun to disintegrate around her.

'Let's just hope he's got more nephews to get themselves engaged,' giggled a woman guest walking by with a glass of champagne. 'Then we'll have this every day!'

'Beth—'

'Cisco, is this true?' she demanded distractedly. 'Is this Jaime they're talking about?'

Cisco had looked everywhere but at her, she remembered numbly.

'Don Filipe's nephew has recently become betrothed,' he stated hoarsely. 'And yes—he has only one nephew. Beth—'

The ringing of the telephone silenced him and Beth

walked over to it, as she had every evening since Jaime had been away.

'Beth, there's something I have to tell you.'

The strained hesitancy in his voice told her it all. 'Oh, you mean your engagement?' she exclaimed with a flippancy that astounded her. 'We're all happily drinking champagne here, courtesy of your uncle Filipe, in celebration.'

'Dear God,' he groaned. 'Beth, I didn't mean you to find out like that. I—'

Her deepest fears confirmed by those few words, she replaced the receiver and Cisco caught her as her legs buckled beneath her.

She barely knew Cisco and the last time she would ever see him would be the following day when he handed her over into Rosita's comforting arms. Yet Francisco Suarez proved to be the most supportive of friends when she most needed one. He arranged for someone to cover for him in the bar and took her to a secluded outcrop of rocks by the bay. When the agonizing immediacy of her grief finally subsided it was Cisco who held her and talked to her, listening to her distraught outpourings and gradually helping her towards a semblance of calm.

Beth rocked now as she clutched the pillow to her, her face tense and drawn.

Cisco had worried about her returning to the villa in the state she was in, especially given that one of June's interminable parties would be in full swing. Beth's thoughts had instantly turned to the gracious Spanish woman with whom she had felt so strong a rapport despite their age difference, and to the peaceful home she had already twice visited. But even if she had had means of getting to Pollensa, where

Rosita lived, and even if it hadn't been getting so late, her pride would have blanked out such thoughts, despite her certainty she would be welcomed with open arms.

'It looks as though you and I are going to a party,' Cisco had said, smiling encouragingly at her. 'And, damn it, we'll have a ball!'

It had been the nightmare to end all nightmares, remembered Beth with a shudder. Cisco had been appalled by the drunken revelry that had greeted them, but not nearly as appalled as June had been by the sight of Beth clinging to the arm of the man on whom she had set her sights. When what June was thinking had finally penetrated Beth's numbed senses, she had approached her by the pool to explain. June's drink-befuddled reaction had been to lunge at Beth; when Cisco had tried to intervene, all three had ended up in the swimming pool. With the raucous cheers of the other party-goers ringing in her ears, Beth had led Cisco to her room, wishing she had drowned.

'I'm sorry…your clothes are ruined,' she choked. 'I feel so terrible you've been subjected to—'

'Beth, none of this is your fault,' Cisco interrupted gently. 'The clothes will dry eventually and so will I—with the aid of a towel.'

Distraught and babbling apologies, Beth urged him into the adjoining shower room, then stripped herself of her wet clothes and put on a bathrobe.

But when Cisco emerged from the shower, clad in a bath towel, she was huddled on the bed, sobbing her heart out.

'You can't stay here,' he said, sitting on the edge of the bed and stroking her soaked hair. 'Is there anywhere you could go tomorrow?' Chokingly Beth mentioned Rosita. 'Right, I'll see if I can borrow a friend's car and take you there in the morning.'

It was at that point that June stormed into the bedroom, screeching abuse.

'Out!' Cisco ordered, and locked the door once he had bustled her out. 'That's settled it—I'm staying,' he stated quietly. 'I'm not leaving you to that, and besides, my clothes will probably take the rest of the night to dry.'

While Beth cried her heart out, Cisco lay down beside her and cradled her to him until at last she calmed down. It was in that position that they both eventually fell asleep and in that position that Jaime found them when, in the small hours of the morning and with June egging him to do so, he shouldered open the bedroom door.

Beth stiffened as though she were seeing it now...the picture of outraged disbelief on Jaime's face as she and Cisco had struggled upright.

A string of expletives had exploded from Jaime and for one instant she had thought he was about to hurl himself on them in his fury.

'My God,' he spat, visibly restraining himself, 'to think I actually believed I owed you an explanation!'

Damning though the circumstantial evidence undoubtedly was, he didn't hesitate for one moment before contemptuously condemning her. It was the instant totality of his condemnation of her that goaded her into giving venomous credence to the lie he had so readily believed.

'You owe me nothing, Jaime,' she flung back at him. 'As you can see, you weren't the only one with a guilty secret... And now everything's out in the open!'

It was the fury and contempt glittering in the eyes that swept across her partially exposed breasts that made her aware that her robe had worked itself loose and she felt her fingernails gouge into the palms of her hands now, as they had then. She could no longer recall what perverse reasoning had prevented her from tightening the robe, but then it had seemed a vital point of honour.

'How long has this been going on?' Jaime had rasped, his voice hoarse with disdain.

'Is that really any business of yours?' Cisco asked curtly, offering tacit support to the lie he had every right to deny.

'No, not really,' Jaime drawled, before adding with scathing contempt, 'I was merely curious as to how long after I had, as they say, deflowered her she waited before deciding to test her new-found skills elsewhere.'

Sounds in the corridor brought Beth hurtling back to the present and seconds later the room seemed to fill. Her heart in her mouth, she leapt to her feet, her eyes fixed on her son as the surgeon and anaesthetist she had met earlier, assisted by Catalina, transferred his limp little form from the trolley to the bed.

'Well, that's a nasty little problem nicely out of the way,' murmured the surgeon, beaming at Beth as, unable to utter a word, she reached a trembling hand towards Jacey. 'Everything went like clockwork,' he added. 'It was—' He broke off, his smile broadening as Jaime strode into the room. 'I'm relieved to tell you, my friend, that even you couldn't have done a neater job,' he chuckled.

Jaime hugged both men and thanked them profusely. He then went to the side of the bed opposite Beth and leaned over his son, his eyes never leaving the small face as he interrogated each man on every detail of what had taken place in the operating theatre.

'All that medical jargon,' whispered Catalina to Beth, rolling her eyes. 'What it boils down to is that Jacey's come through his op brilliantly—as anyone can see.' She gave Beth's arm an encouraging squeeze before stepping back from her.

As Jaime finished eliciting every last dreg of information from his colleagues, he began patting Jacey firmly on the cheeks.

'You'll wake him,' protested Beth, at last finding her voice.

'That's precisely what I want to do.' Jaime grinned, his eyes suddenly catching Beth's with a look that struck a long-forgotten chord in her, leaving her trembling with the force of it. 'Come on, little hero,' he urged tenderly. 'It's time you woke up.'

Beth was unconsciously holding her breath as Jacey began stirring. His head turned slightly, as though irritated by his father's firm touch, then his eyes fluttered open.

'Hello, sleepyhead,' murmured Beth, barely noticing the other two doctors take their leave of Jaime and slip from the room.

'Mamá...Papá.' He turned his head, as though searching. 'Yaya?'

'Yaya's had to go to tidy the gallery, remember?' whispered Beth.

He nodded, his eyes closing again.

'Hey—we're not having you doze off on us again,' teased his father.

'Course I'm not,' muttered Jacey with drowsy irritability. 'My tummy's still sore,' he added accusingly.

'As I told you it would be,' stated Jaime. 'But I also told you it would be a different sort of pain—was I right?'

The child nodded, pulling a face, then turned to his mother. 'I've got stitches and they're very sore,' he explained solemnly. His face crumpled. 'They're very sore, Mamá!'

Jaime murmured something to Catalina. 'So, what shall we prescribe for something very sore?' he asked his son.

'A 'pository, I suppose,' was the tearful reply.

'And you suppose right,' murmured Jaime, taking the dish the nurse handed him.

Beth watched as he gently tended to their son, her heart breaking quietly inside her. Giving her thoughts such freedom had been a madness she should never have succumbed to, she remonstrated with herself hopelessly; her wounds were as fresh now as the day they had been inflicted and she felt drained to the point of exhaustion.

Later she slipped away and rang Rosita, and when she returned she hadn't the energy to argue when Jaime again remarked on how thoroughly tired she looked and insisted on ordering a car and a driver to take her back to his house.

CHAPTER SIX

IT WAS dark when Beth awoke and several hours of dreamless sleep had gone some way to restoring her spirits.

There was no denying that the vividness of her memories, on top of the strain of Jacey's operation, had taken it out of her, she reflected as she took an invigoratingly cold shower. But she had needed the harshness of remembering to help combat the terrible folly of still loving Jaime.

Glistening from the shower, she slipped into a loose towelling robe, a smile creeping to her lips. Jacey was her life and he had come through the operation safely; nothing else mattered.

She belted the robe tightly around her, removed the shower cap and ran her fingers through her hair, then padded barefoot down the stairs. She went into the kitchen and began filling the kettle, starting when she heard her name called out.

'Jaime, I didn't hear you coming!' she exclaimed as he appeared in the doorway. 'I was just about to make coffee—would you like some?'

'To hell with coffee,' he replied, grinning from ear to ear. 'Tonight calls for champagne.'

'Champagne?' echoed Beth, her eyes widening with disbelief. There was a look about him she had never seen before and found impossible to pinpoint. 'Jaime, are you sure you haven't been drinking already?'

He burst out laughing. 'Come to think of it, I feel as though I have—but I can assure you I haven't. It's just that I find that son of ours amazing…simply amazing!'

'What—?'

'Hang on a moment,' he muttered, then turned on his heel and disappeared.

Feeling totally bemused, Beth sat down on a kitchen stool, hugging her arms around her and wondering what on earth was going on.

'Here we are!' exclaimed Jaime, returning with a bottle of champagne which he stuffed into the freezer. 'Probably not the best treatment for such a vintage, or any other, for that matter, but—'

'Jaime,' she begged. 'Tell me what you meant about Jacey… Tell me what's going on, for heaven's sake.'

He flashed her an apologetic grin. 'I'm sorry, Beth… I'm on this incredible high and I just can't seem to come down from it. I'm also in dire need of a shower,' he chuckled, then strode over and grabbed her by the hand. Completely ignoring her protests, he dragged her up the stairs behind him and into his room. 'You sit there while I shower,' he instructed her, giving her a light push onto the bed before peeling off his shirt. 'And I'll fill you in with the latest on that miracle child of ours.'

Before Beth could blink, let alone make any response, he had disappeared into the adjoining bathroom, leaving the door open behind him.

'Once he'd slept off the anaesthetic, he was fighting fit,' he bellowed over the noise of the gushing water. 'And demanding to see his appendix in a jar!'

Beth tried to steel herself against the warmth melt-

ing through her. Jaime Caballeros, the doting father...
Never in her wildest dreams could she have imagined
this.

'We've had to put him on antibiotics because his
temperature was slightly raised and—'

'He's running a temperature?' gasped Beth.
'Jaime—'

'That's fairly common, I promise you, and nothing
to be concerned about,' he cut in reassuringly. 'Mind
you, he wasn't the least bit happy about having to
have an injection this evening.' He chuckled, the ease
of his laughter reassuring her far more than words
ever could. 'Though tomorrow he'll be able to have
them orally.' He strolled back into the bedroom,
black-robed and vigorously drying his hair, then
halted, something deeper and darker than mere surprise momentarily sparking in his eyes as he caught
sight of Beth sitting on the edge of the large bed. 'I
must sound like a gibbering idiot to you—reacting
like this,' he muttered, the wild elation that had
buoyed him ever since his arrival noticeably faltering.

Beth rose to her feet, feeling as though she had
been punched in the stomach. It had been the jubilant
father who had so unthinkingly dragged her up here,
she thought defeatedly, but it was the man who, to
his horror, could still feel desire for her standing before her now.

'I'll wait for you downstairs,' she said, successfully
eliminating the crushing bitterness she was feeling
from her tone. Desiring someone you hated was one
thing; loving the person you should hate was another
matter altogether.

'So you're not denying you think I'm a gibbering
idiot?' he asked, the tension softening in him.

'Jaime, I—'

'Please, Beth… Let me explain.'

'Jaime, you don't have to explain anything.'

'How can you say that before you have any idea what I want to say?' he demanded exasperatedly.

'Perhaps I do have an idea,' she retorted stiffly, then burst out, 'Jacey's mother and I—we're not two separate people, no matter how you choose to see things!'

He gave her a startled look. 'But you've had so much more practice than I have,' he muttered uncertainly.

Now it was Beth's turn to look startled; she hadn't the slightest idea what he meant. 'Perhaps you'd better explain,' she conceded edgily.

'Thank you,' he snapped, then added baldly, 'My father died of peritonitis—his appendix ruptured.'

'Oh, Jaime!' gasped Beth, flopping dazedly back onto the bed.

'I felt it would be wrong, under the circumstances, to tell you about it when you first learned he had died,' he muttered. 'But I wasn't prepared for the way it became distorted in my mind once I realized Jacey was my son.'

'Jaime, how did it happen?' she asked, belated awareness of how badly she had misread what he had been about to say only now hitting her.

'He was on tour in an East African game reserve and thought he'd picked up a stomach bug. By the time it was realized it was no bug and he was taken to a Nairobi hospital, he had already ruptured… Any fool could see there was no point of similarity whatever between his case and Jacey's—' He broke off, giving a dazed shake of his head before continuing.

'Well, not quite *any* fool…especially not one whose medical training seemed to have flown out of the window. Perhaps with practice the father and the doctor will blend into one, but I haven't mastered it yet.'

'Oh, Jaime, what can I say?' asked Beth huskily, her heart aching for him.

'Nothing preferably,' he said, his smile diffident, almost embarrassed as he reached for her hand. 'So, let's see if that champagne has survived my monstrous treatment, shall we?' This time his smile was more positive and once more Beth found herself being dragged by the hand after him.

She watched him retrieve the bottle from the freezer, her mind a welter of conflicting sensations. 'So tell me, how bad a fight did Jacey actually put up over the injection?' she asked, respecting his obvious wish not to speak further about his father.

'Well…he tried a spot of blackmail initially,' he laughed. 'We need glasses—they're in the dining-room cabinet,' he said, giving her a gentle push in that direction.

'How, exactly, did he try to blackmail you?' she asked, returning with two tall crystal glasses.

'By informing me his *mamá* would be cross with me,' he grinned, stripping the foil from the bottle, then aiming it at her.

'Jaime, don't you dare!' she shrieked, ducking.

'But I told him his *mamá* would be even crosser with me if I didn't give him the injection and he ended up with an infection.' There was devilment in his grin as the cork flew past Beth, ominously close to her.

'You've just wasted a third of that,' she laughed, infected by his mood as she steered the glasses to catch the foaming liquid he was spraying everywhere.

'I rang Rosita before I left to give her the latest on Jacey,' he announced, his eyes twinkling as he raised his glass, 'and she insisted on being remembered in any toasts we might be drinking. To Rosita.'

'To Rosita,' echoed Beth, not even stopping to wonder that he and Rosita had decided to dispense with formalities as she drank thirstily.

'And to Jaime Carlos—Jacey—who would also wish to be included.'

By the time they had finished toasting just about everyone even remotely connected with the removal of Jacey's appendix, Beth was feeling weak from laughter and decidedly light-headed.

'Oh, I forgot to tell you!' exclaimed Jaime. 'I've invited Rosita here to dinner tomorrow, by way of a celebration.'

'That's very kind of you,' said Beth, and would have drunk to it had she not already drained her glass.

Jaime chuckled. 'It'll please Gisela, my house-keeper; she's always complaining about how little en-tertaining I do.' He eyed her across the kitchen table with a lazy, lopsided grin. 'That reminds me—have you eaten anything, Beth?'

Beth shook her head and found it swimming alarmingly.

'Neither have I... I don't actually feel like anything, but perhaps you should have something.'

'Probably,' agreed Beth, 'but I'm not in the least hungry.'

He gave another soft chuckle. 'Well, at least this champagne hasn't been laced with a sedative,' he teased. 'Hell, I've just remembered—I have to go up north in the morning to check up on my road accident victim and her baby.'

'Your what?' queried Beth woozily.

'She insisted on being taken to her local hospital,' he explained vaguely. 'But don't worry, I've done all the surgery I'll be performing on her... Luckily for her,' he added, grinning as he refilled their glasses, slopping what was left of the champagne everywhere as he imitated a badly shaking hand. 'It's all very well laughing,' he reproved as Beth dissolved into giggles, 'but would you let this man operate on you?'

'Jaime, what sort of surgery did you perform on the poor woman anyway?'

'Another doctor and I did a bit of work on her leg, which had been trapped—then I got on with the Caesarian section... A beautiful little girl called Beth.'

'Now I know you're making all this up,' she giggled.

'Making it up?' he exclaimed indignantly. 'The mother was so happy she said I could name the baby. I could hardly name a girl after me... And Beth is such a beautiful name.'

'I'm still not sure I believe you,' she smiled, raising her glass to her lips, then deciding she had had more than enough as it was.

'Well, it serves you right if you're overcome with guilt when you read of my heroic feats in tomorrow's papers,' he grinned. 'And I shall expect you to be up bright and early to read them all to my son in my absence—so, to bed!' He took her hand across the table and coaxed her to her feet. 'I'm sure he'll believe it, even if you don't.'

'I suppose even I would believe it if I saw it in print,' giggled Beth as she followed him from the kitchen and up the stairs.

'I've a good mind to tell the mother I've changed

my mind about the name,' he threatened as they reached the top of the staircase.

'Is she going to be all right—the mother?' asked Beth. 'I mean, you said her leg was—'

'She'll be fine. They'll just be tidying up her leg tomorrow, not that it was seriously damaged... And don't think I haven't noticed how you've changed the subject,' he informed her with a lazy laugh, halting suddenly and swinging round to face her.

He reached out and took one of her hands to steady her as she stumbled against him. The laughter had gone from his eyes when he drew that hand to his mouth and nuzzled his lips gently against it.

Beth heard her own sharp intake of breath as need leapt hotly within her.

'Beth,' he breathed huskily. He caught her to him, his mouth plundering hers with hot, groaning kisses that sparked a fierce answering hunger. 'I... It doesn't matter,' he whispered barely coherently against her mouth. 'You know that, don't you? Nothing matters...'

Several times, after that long-ago first explosive union of their bodies, they had bemusedly attempted to account for the magic that had possessed them. It had continued to possess them, no matter what the circumstances of their love-making, and soon they had given up seeking that elusive answer, confident in the permanence of a magic that never failed.

Now, as they stumbled in a passionate embrace into his bedroom, tearing their robes from around one another, Beth was startled to find her mind momentarily crystal-clear, placing that familiar magic on temporary hold to ask one question. A question no sooner asked than answered, allowing the magic to take over and leaving their minds behind as their bodies shuddered in fevered anticipation of rediscovering the joys so long denied them.

'Beth, we'll have to stop a moment while I get something,' he muttered hoarsely, his hands roaming in distracted exploration of the body trembling against his.

She shook her head. 'No, it's all right—you don't have to,' she whispered, reiterating the answer she had already given to her own question.

He lifted her against him, his body, as always, infallible in its interpretation of the impassioned demands of hers, then swung down onto the bed, carrying her with him.

His hands shook as they moved against her in an urgent, intimate caress and a sharp cry exploded from him at the uninhibited intensity of the response they instantly encountered.

'Can it really still be like this?' he groaned as his body answered the fevered demands of hers and plunged deep into its creamy depths.

'Yes!' she cried, the laughter of the girl she had once been bubbling from deep within her as the first of a barrage of increasingly powerful waves of erotic sensation pounded through her.

'It's not fair,' he had once breathlessly complained. 'It keeps happening to you, whereas I can only…' His words had been lost in the frenzy of the tempest engulfing them.

And now, as it always had been then, it was at the point at which passion stripped the last of his reason from him, exploding within her and filling her with the hot surge of its potency, that her own body was carried to the dizzying heights of total fulfilment.

Then and there, here and now—they were all a hazy jumble as their bodies clung, glistening and panting in the aftermath of a magic that was timeless.

Then there had been no tears; now they slid silently down her cheeks. And when he wordlessly kissed them away she whispered his name and felt his need for her stir once more and grow powerfully within her.

For a while tenderness restrained the wildness of their mutual need as they kissed and sought out all the familiar erotic secrets they had once shared. When the tenderness became no longer bearable, they abandoned themselves to the explosive passion that left them spent and gasping in one another's arms.

When at last he turned, as he had done so often before in those careless days of rapture, carrying her with him until she lay on top of him along the length of his body, she rested her head against the matt dampness of his chest while his arms curved around her.

Tomorrow she would have no option but to face reality, she accepted as her eyes became heavy with sleep...but tonight she was once more the nineteen-year-old, in love for ever.

CHAPTER SEVEN

'PAPÁ might have to give you an injection,' Jacey sternly informed his mother as she tidied away the game the three of them had been playing. 'You look tireder than me, doesn't she, Yaya?'

'I'm afraid I can only agree with you, my darling,' murmured Rosita, amusement mingling with anxiety on her kindly features. 'Which is why I was just about to suggest I take her back to Papá's house and make her have a good long siesta... Do you think that's a good idea?'

Jacey nodded, his eyes inspecting his mother as he threw himself with relish into the role of guardian of her well-being. 'I think it's a *very* good idea,' he informed Beth gravely. 'Because otherwise you might fall asleep during the supper Papá's going to cook for you and Yaya tonight and that would be very rude, wouldn't it?'

Beth managed to compose her features into an expression of equal gravity, while her mind grappled with the likelihood of Jaime finding an excuse not to turn up for the meal to which he had invited Rosita. 'You're right, it would be very rude,' she said, glancing down at her watch. 'And as it's just about time for *your* siesta, I suppose Yaya might as well drive me back for mine now.' She tucked him up and kissed him. 'Just you wait till those stitches are out—I'm going to give you the biggest squeeze you've ever had,' she whispered softly.

He began to chuckle, but broke off in wincing pro-test. 'You're not supposed to make me laugh… It's very extremely sore when I do. You'd better tell Papá, before he comes, in case he forgets too.'

'Don't you worry, I'll tell him,' promised Rosita, bending over and kissing him. 'Now, I'll be back later, once I've got your *mamá* tucked up… So off you go to sleep.'

'But you won't forget to tell Papá, will you?' he demanded sleepily.

Rosita reassured him she wouldn't and kissed him again, her eyes moist as she followed Beth from the room. 'It's such a relief to have that operation safely behind him,' she muttered, her voice unsteady.

Beth reached for Rosita's hand and squeezed it. 'Every instinct I possess told me he was going to be all right,' she said, 'but now and then I'd find myself wondering if it weren't simply a case of wishful think-ing.'

Rosita flashed her a troubled look as they left the building and made towards the car park. 'I can safely say that I never experienced so much as a twinge of doubt regarding Jacey,' she stated quietly. 'But I wish I could say the same where you're concerned,' she added as she began rummaging in her handbag for her car keys.

Beth found herself biting back the trite words of reassurance automatically forming on her lips while at the same time wondering what she could trust her-self to say. Certainly not the truth, she thought numbly. Right now, the truth was something she had yet fully to come to terms with herself, let alone at-tempt to share it—even with Rosita. One of the few coherent things Jaime had said last night was that nothing mattered; and for her nothing *had* mattered—except the all-consuming need he had aroused in her. But the fact that she still loved him beyond all reason was no excuse for the way she had deceived him about being suitably protected, nor for allowing the utter annihilation of any claim she had to pride or self-respect... The fact that he had given in to his physical need for her last night could never erase the fury of rejection that had been in his eyes when he had first realized the extent to which he could still lust after her. And that was why this morning shouldn't have come as such a shock to her.

But it had, she reminded herself bitterly as she got into the car. She had no idea when he had left, but he had gone without so much as a word, leaving her to awaken alone in his bed... To face the reality she had so willingly turned her back on the night before.

Rosita inserted the key in the ignition but instead of starting the car she turned to Beth. 'Darling, the more I think about it, the more I realize what a mistake our rarely, if ever, mentioning Jaime was. Deep down I've always known it was wrong of me not to attempt to break the taboo and—'

'Wrong of *you,* Rosita?' protested Beth, aghast. 'All you ever did was go along with what I wanted.'

'And I shouldn't have,' stated Rosita firmly. 'It left you so terribly unprepared for when you actually did meet him. Darling, not only were you unaware that he hadn't married, you had actually fretted over the thought that he might have had other children.'

'Yes, but—'

'No, Beth, there aren't any buts—I should have told you,' Rosita cut in firmly. 'Just as I should have told you the truth about the other women he became involved with after his fiancée died. You suggested that perhaps he was searching for a replacement for her, yet my response was noncommittal, despite my knowing that he had always made a point of telling those women that that was precisely what he was not looking for.'

The heat in the small car was almost stifling, but Beth felt suddenly chilled to the bone.

'You know how I feel about gossip, and the drivel some of those gossip columnists came up with about you at times only strengthened such feelings,' continued the older woman, her tone strained and uneasy. 'And when rumours of Jaime's out-and-out womanizing started appearing in the press here—'

'It got into the papers?' gasped Beth.

Rosita nodded. 'For almost a year, up until he went to South America, there were frequent reports concerning his carryings on... With his background, wealth and looks, he's an extremely eligible young man. I was simply thankful you were away on modelling assignments so often during that period and consequently missed coming across those reports.'

'But there's more than newspaper gossip involved,' stated Beth, a sick dread filling her.

Again the woman beside her nodded. 'While Jaime was still in Madrid, the niece of an old friend of mine fell in love with him. Inez, the aunt, was halfway into telling me the story before I realized the identity of the man involved. The girl—Lorena, I believe her name is—got a position as physiotherapist at the hospital Jaime worked in and soon heard of his reputation as a heart-breaker. According to Inez she would have had to be deaf not to... But it didn't stop the young woman falling in love with him.'

'Jaime can be pretty irresistible when he puts his mind to it!' exclaimed Beth hoarsely, her entire body now shaking as though from the cold.

'It seems it wasn't a case of that,' sighed Rosita. 'He was as brutally honest with her as he allegedly was with all the others. But after she had seen him a few times the poor girl decided to be honest with him and tell him how she felt... And Jaime was extremely upset.'

'Oh, I'm sure he was,' burst out Beth acidly. Jaime liked to have what he wanted with no strings attached, as his slinking off without a word that morning had so clearly indicated.

'Darling, please hear me out,' pleaded Rosita, her kindly face drawn with anxiety. 'It was on Lorena's behalf that he was so upset. He told her he would give his right arm to be able to love someone like her...but that he was a man who could love only once and that love was now lost to him. A few months later he left for South America and threw himself into setting up a series of clinics for the poor.'

'I... Why have you told me all this?' asked Beth, her mouth so dry it was a struggle to get the words out.

'I wish I could say for sure,' sighed Rosita, her expression troubled. 'Possibly because I suspect you're still very vulnerable where Jaime's concerned, and feel you should know exactly what you're up against.'

'Your friend's niece knew exactly what she was up against,' stated Beth tonelessly, 'but that didn't stop her from falling in love with him.'

Rosita pulled a small face, then started up the car. 'True; but she got over him. The last I heard from

Inez was that Lorena had just got engaged and was on top of the world.'

'I'm glad there was a happy ending,' said Beth as they drove off, managing a wan smile. 'But it does make me wonder whether she truly was in love with Jaime in the first place.'

Rosita flashed her an unreadable look. 'You believe that Jaime is right, do you?' she asked. 'That you just get the one chance at love?'

Beth shrugged. 'Perhaps that's all that some people get.'

Those like herself and Jaime, she thought numbly, who were doomed to love but once.

'Or perhaps that's just what some people manage to convince themselves is all they get,' muttered Rosita, swerving to avoid a wobbling cyclist. 'And when otherwise sane and healthy young people hold such views it strikes me as not only a terrible waste, but also as downright unnatural!' She glanced over at Beth. 'I suppose there was never going to be a right time or place for me to say my piece,' she sighed, 'but I've a feeling I couldn't have chosen worse... You really do look exhausted, darling.'

'I'll be fine after a sleep,' replied Beth. 'But I'm glad you told me what you did... No, really I am,' she protested as Rosita flashed her a sceptical look. 'It puts certain things into perspective... And I needed that.'

'I hope so,' muttered Rosita, turning into the drive of the house. She shook her head when Beth suggested she come in for a coffee. 'And you're not to have one either,' she admonished sternly. 'You're to go straight to your bed and get some sleep.' She reached over suddenly and hugged Beth. 'One of these days you're going to find the happiness you deserve,' she whispered emotionally. 'Just you remember that… Now off you go and get some sleep.'

Feeling numb and peculiarly detached, Beth let herself into the house. She went to the kitchen to tell the housekeeper she had returned, but refused the woman's offer of coffee.

It was as she reached the foot of the stairs that she halted and gave an angry toss of her head. Why was she behaving as though Rosita had told her anything she didn't already know? Up until now all she had done was refuse to face the fact of Jaime's undying love for the woman so tragically taken from him. Even in the face of his angry reaction to discovering he still physically desired her, and despite the inescapable message of this morning's wordless disappearance, she had closed her mind to that irrefutable fact. She wasn't the same as those other women, with whom he had at least been honest; she was the woman with whom he had been unfaithful to his one and only love, and for that he would never forgive her.

She began mounting the stairs, then froze at the sound of the front door closing. She turned round, the breath catching in her throat as she saw Jaime approach the foot of the stairs.

'What are you doing here?' The words burst from her, senseless and unplanned and harshly accusing.

'Me?' he drawled, halting mid-stride, his expression glacial, his eyes darkening with fury. 'I live here—remember?'

'I… You know what I meant,' gabbled Beth, struggling to gain some sort of a grip on herself. 'I thought you were seeing a patient…'

'I saw her. And now I'm here to pick up something before going to the clinic.'

He stood there, his expression remote, his coldly detached gaze that of a hostile stranger. Yet it was the body of this distant, physically beautiful stranger that had so exquisitely punished hers in the fierceness of passion throughout the previous night, his hoarse cries of pleasure that had blended so often with her own during those long, dark hours.

'Well, I'll not keep you,' she muttered, turning in a distracted attempt to flee her own thoughts. 'I'm going to have a rest.'

'Now that we're both here, don't you think it would be wise for us to talk?' he asked.

Beth spun round, pride alone containing the anger his coolly forbidding tone had sparked in her. 'Jaime, you're the one with the problem regarding last night.' The cool dismissal ringing in her words brought her equal measures of astonishment and relief. 'And talking to me isn't going to solve it.'

'And you have no problem regarding last night?' His face was remote and expressionless now, but an edge of steel sliced through his words.

'Nothing that a couple of hours' sleep won't cure,' she retorted, then turned her back on him and continued her way up the stairs.

She had barely reached the top when she experienced a sensation of almost being flung from her feet. The next thing she knew she was slammed against a wall, with Jaime's towering, glowering presence blocking her escape.

'And what do you think my problem is?' he demanded, his hands spread against the wall on either side of her to brace the body trapping hers, his eyes blazing their fury.

Too stunned by the explosive suddenness of what had happened to feel any fear, Beth simply raised her gaze to his.

'Answer me!' he ordered, his eyes burning down into hers.

Beth took a breath and felt it catch in her throat as the anger surging within her was transformed into a white-hot rage of desire. And in that same instant she saw the eyes locked with hers widen with momentary shock as their green-flecked depths betrayed a hunger to match her own.

'Damn you, Beth, answer me!' he groaned, the sultry heat of his gaze now dropping to the mouth on which still lingered tell-tale traces of the previous night's passion.

She could sense the battle taking place in him, even as his head lowered fractionally towards hers. And she was fighting her own fierce struggle with arms that longed to reach out to him, with a body aching to take that one step that would bring it into contact with the lean hardness of his.

She felt the heat of his breath, hot and sweet against her skin, with the angry expletive that exploded from him as he pushed himself back from the wall and away from her.

'And there you have your problem in a nutshell,' she flung at him, her breath ragged as though from a long, gruelling run, her body shaking uncontrollably. 'You can't stand the fact that you still want me physically.'

'I can't say it was something I expected,' he said, the drawling dismissal in his tone at odds with the stark pallor of his features and the tension visibly clenching his jaw. 'But I'd say that last night more than proved that I've overcome my initial surprise. Let's face it, Beth, you are an extremely desirable woman and I'm just a normal, red-blooded man.'

'I'm sure there are plenty of women around who can confirm your red-bloodedness,' Beth retorted, shaken more by his apparent inability to acknowledge the truth than the deliberately insulting tone of his words. 'But I wonder how many of them would consider you normal!'

The look he gave her was scowlingly baleful but his tone was chilling as he spoke. 'Obviously not the ones you've come across.'

'Oh, I haven't come across any of them,' retorted Beth, the realization that she had scored a hit partially restoring her composure. 'It's just that you've had rather a bad press where your love life is concerned.'

'Where my sex life is concerned,' he corrected her with icy venom. 'I don't have a love life.' He rammed his clenched hands deep into his pockets as he leaned back against the landing railings and glowered across at her. 'But at least the press reports on me are consistent—whereas with you they can't seem to make their minds up whether you're an ice maiden or the female equivalent of me.' He paused, then smiled—a stunning, heart-stoppingly beautiful smile so contrived that it sent a shiver of fear through her. 'But I know which you are, don't I, Beth? Though you needn't worry—your secret is safe with me.'

'I've had enough of this,' she muttered, close to breaking point. 'If you don't mind, I'm going to have a rest.'

'And I must get back to the clinic,' announced

Jaime, removing his hands from his pockets and straightening. 'But there's just one thing before I go, Beth… If you thought I had such a problem about wanting you sexually, how is it you spent last night with me?'

Beth reached her hand back against the wall to brace herself as shock waves rippled through her. 'Easy,' she replied, lowering her head as she felt the colour drain from her face. 'You're an extremely desirable man and I'm just a normal, red-blooded woman.'

She had no idea how she made it to her room, but once there she collapsed on the bed, tears of anger and sorrow and humiliation choking from her.

Once she had believed that nothing could be worse than the pain he had inflicted on her all those years ago, but this savage reopening of wounds never fully healed was undermining that belief… She had to get him out of her life, before she was destroyed completely.

While Rosita and Jaime discussed a Miro painting hanging at the far end of the elegant drawing room, Beth surreptitiously examined him, an untouched aperitif in her hand. The perfect host, she thought: erudite, charming and witty. Yet not once since he and Rosita had arrived had he addressed her in any terms other than general and not once had his eyes made full contact with hers.

That she had actually slept after their disturbing encounter had surprised her, but she had woken in a very different frame of mind from that in which she'd sunk into exhausted sleep. The fact that she still loved Jaime was a nightmare beyond her control, she accepted, but there was no way she would allow it to destroy her. The vulnerable, penniless nineteen-year-old had survived to find fame and success... And that was what she seemed to have lost track of during these past traumatic days—that she wasn't the helpless victim she had once been, she was now a strong, independent woman with the means to do whatever she chose.

'Once my painters become established, I don't exhibit them at the gallery,' Rosita was explaining to Jaime when a maid appeared to announce that dinner was served. 'My Miguel never forgot the terrible struggle he had to find anywhere that would exhibit him in the early days,' she continued, walking over to Beth and linking arms with her as they made their way towards the dining room. 'Which is why, when he achieved fame, he started up the gallery to give promising young unknowns a chance.'

'And most of them don't remain unknowns for very long once you've exhibited them,' murmured Jaime, walking beside the two women. 'You obviously have as keen an eye for talent as your late husband.'

'Never as keen as Miguel's,' protested Rosita, smiling as she took her seat at the dining table. 'I rely heavily on the advice of very knowledgeable friends... And the odd flash of genius from those allegedly not so knowledgeable,' she added with a chuckle, smiling over at Beth. 'It was Beth who first spotted Pedro Rivera.'

The dark wings of Jaime's eyebrows arched in surprise and for the first time that evening his eyes actually met Beth's. 'Now there really is a name to conjure with,' he murmured, his gaze almost mocking in its coolness. 'I believe I read somewhere that Laurens Morante is making a film based on Rivera's life.'

'Based exceedingly loosely on his life,' chuckled Rosita, while Beth, suspecting what was coming, felt herself cringe. 'It seems that Laurens Morante has always secretly yearned to direct an out and out love story—and who could blame the poor man, given the tortured realism of most of his films—?' She broke off to shake her head as Jaime offered her wine. 'No, thanks—I'm driving. But don't let that stop you two!' she exclaimed, when Beth also refused and Jaime poured himself some water from a pitcher on the table.

'Don't worry, it won't,' said Beth, awareness of a hint of anxiety in Rosita's gaze forcing a smile to her lips. 'It's just that I don't feel much like wine at the moment.'

'And I'll be sticking to this,' said Jaime, indicating the water, 'because, unfortunately, I'm on call this evening… So, what was that you were saying about Laurens Morante?'

'Ah, the love story,' smiled Rosita. 'He got to hear about Beth's role in Pedro's discovery and decided to use that as the romantic angle. He also wanted Beth to star as herself in his film and pestered the life out of her before finally, and most reluctantly, accepting her refusal.'

'Really?' murmured Jaime, his face an expressionless mask. 'I'm sure there must be scores of established stars who would sell their souls to be in one of Morante's films.'

Beth gave her attention to the food being served, wondering if she was imagining the sudden tension in an atmosphere that hadn't exactly been light from the start.

'So why *did* you turn down the offer?' Jaime persisted blandly.

'Because I have no desire whatever to be an actress,' retorted Beth, the conviction that he was attempting to bait her making her hackles rise.

'But surely modelling is in many ways a form of acting,' observed Jaime, his tone verging on caustic.

'I've never regarded it as such,' retorted Beth frigidly. 'But, as you may or may not be aware, I had no desire whatever to be a model either.'

'So why did you become one?' drawled Jaime, seemingly oblivious of Rosita's look of wide-eyed concern.

'That's something that someone with your background of privilege and wealth would find virtually impossible to comprehend—having to give up what you most wanted in life simply to earn a living.'

Beth heard Rosita's sharp intake of breath, but she no longer cared. Earlier, when she had tried confronting him with the unpleasant truth of his feelings towards her, he had taken the coward's way out and mockingly dodged the issue. But now, with Rosita his unwitting shield against any retaliation, he was letting her know just how ghastly a mistake he considered the previous night to have been. And, despicable coward though he must know himself to be, he still had no qualms about looking down his aristocratic nose and passing judgement on her from the security of his ivory tower.

'Perhaps even you might have heard of Tom Jordan—it was his photographs of me that launched my reluctant career and started him on the path to being one of the most successful photographers around. But when I first met Tom he was a struggling student and I was virtually penniless,' she continued relentlessly. 'Have you any idea what poverty is? Inescapable, soul-destroying poverty?' she demanded. 'When Tom spent hour after hour taking photographs of me, a career in modelling or anything else was the last thing on my mind—I needed to *eat*! Have you any idea what lengths I'd have gone to simply to provide the next meal? If there had been a market for nude studies of pregnant women, do you think I wouldn't have stripped?'

Jaime's head had begun moving slowly from side to side while she spoke, as though trying to block out her words.

'Please, Beth,' he begged hoarsely.

'It's only people like you who have the luxury of choice,' she flung at him, deaf to his plea. 'For the rest of us it's often a matter of having to take whatever dirt fate chooses to dish out to us!'

'No, Beth—that's enough!' Rosita reached across and gripped her tightly by the wrist.

Almost as quickly as it had erupted, Beth felt the fury drain from her.

'Why, Beth, why?' demanded Jaime dazedly. 'You were carrying my child, yet you gave me no chance to protect you.'

'That's enough of this—both of you!' exclaimed Rosita sharply. 'I know you've both been through a lot in the past few days, but this is too much.'

'Rosita—I'm so sorry,' said Beth, guilt now flooding her. 'I had no right to drag you into this…I've behaved inexcusably.'

'And I too,' muttered Jaime hoarsely.

Rosita looked from one to the other, shaking her head in weary exasperation. 'I can't deny it upsets me to see you both like this,' she sighed. 'But somehow or other you're going to have to sort yourselves out and come to terms with the past—for your own sakes and, most especially, for Jacey's.' Just as she finished speaking a maid entered and asked if they would like coffee to be served in the drawing room. 'A very good idea,' stated Rosita, rising to her feet. 'I'll have to be going soon, so let's put this behind us for now and enjoy our coffee.'

Brushing aside their contrite attempts to make further apology, the older woman steered the conversation to the one subject guaranteed to hold them: their son. She had even managed to evoke laughter from them by the time the maid returned to tell Jaime he was wanted on the telephone.

Rosita rose to her feet as he made his apologies and left the room. 'It's time I got on my way,' she said, walking over to Beth and hugging her as she too rose.

'I don't know why I behaved as I did earlier,' choked Beth. 'Rosita, I'm so sorry, I—'

'Not half as sorry as I am that I repeated all that gossip to you,' interrupted Rosita with a sigh.

'It wasn't just gossip,' protested Beth as they made their way to the hall. 'And you were right—I needed to know.'

'But that's just it!' exclaimed Rosita agitatedly. 'What do any of us really know? What I told you came second if not third hand. I felt I was doing the right thing, but now the only thing I'm really certain of is that it's Jaime alone who can give you the true story. Beth, you—' She broke off, swinging round as Jaime appeared in the doorway.

'That was the clinic,' he informed them. 'I'm afraid I have to leave right away.'

'And so must I,' said Rosita, smiling over at him. 'And my thanks to you, Jaime, for a truly superb meal.'

'I'll pass your comments on to Gisela, my house-keeper,' he smiled, then, with a small bow, excused himself.

Rosita linked her arm in Beth's as they continued to the hall. 'We'll talk tomorrow if you feel like it,' she said, reaching up and stroking Beth's cheek. 'But you get yourself off to bed now and try to get a good night's rest.'

Beth hugged her and promised she would, then made her way up to her room.

So much for her positive frame of mind, she thought bitterly as she undressed. Tonight she had come very close to snapping completely and in the process had upset Rosita deeply. And as for Rosita's regrets about her earlier disclosures... Holding her head in her hands, Beth sank onto the bed. Rosita had told her little that, in her heart of hearts, she hadn't already known, but had stubbornly refused to accept. And now everything had been put into terrible perspective...

When it came to love she and Jaime were very alike, she accepted reluctantly, remembering how, having lost him, she had been incapable of loving another man. Where they differed was in their attitude to sex, which to her went hand in hand with love. But she was the woman with whom he had been unfaithful to the only one he had loved. And there could be no hiding from the fact that, whatever last night might have meant to her, Jaime plainly regarded it as a further betrayal, for which he would forgive neither himself nor her.

CHAPTER EIGHT

'WHAT a shame Pedro and Jorge didn't meet Papá,' sighed Jacey as his mother and Rosita tidied away the mountain of presents with which his friends had come laden. 'Papá thinks it's a shame too and said he'd love to meet them another time.'

Beth gave him a puzzled look. 'When did Papá say that?' she asked. When she had arrived at the clinic that morning she had been told that Jaime would probably not be back for the rest of the day. Her main feeling had been one of relief.

'He came to see me after you and Yaya went to see Pedro and Jorge and their *mamás* off,' the child replied nonchalantly. 'And he says that if I'm very good I can go home at the end of the week,' he added, beaming benignly. 'Won't that be lovely for you and Yaya?' he demanded, supremely confident of his position at the centre of their world.

'It will be the most wonderful thing that's happened for ages and ages,' replied Beth, hugging him tightly.

'And no doubt the most exhausting,' murmured Rosita wryly, reaching over and ruffling his hair, 'if today's anything to go by. You must be worn out—I know I am and I didn't have you and your friends to contend with all morning.'

'It was really good fun this morning!' exclaimed Jacey enthusiastically. 'Mamá read us all a lovely story from the book José sent me, and then we sang songs with Jorge's *mamá*. I'm really sad you and Papá missed it all. Mamá, let's show Yaya how to play that game Pedro's *mamá* gave me.'

'We'll show her another day,' said Beth firmly, gathering up the several components of one of the many toys showered on him by his wide circle of friends. 'But it's past your bedtime now and we still haven't cleared away all these lovely presents of yours.'

'There are so many of them,' chuckled Rosita, 'it's like Christmas and your birthday rolled into one. Where on earth are we going to put them all?'

'We could put them all into my locker,' suggested Jacey helpfully.

Beth shook her head. 'It's far too small to hold all these,' she said, gesturing towards the mound. 'I was thinking of going back home with Yaya tonight, so I think the best idea is for you to choose one or two presents to keep here with you and for us to take the rest back with us, ready for when you come home.'

Jacey nodded, then set about the task of selecting which of the toys he could bring himself to be temporarily parted from. It was only after several changes of mind that the final choice was made and they began settling him for the night.

'I forgot to tell Papá about you being so tired, Mamá,' he announced out of the blue as Beth began tucking him up. 'I think you must have been naughty and not had a proper siesta yesterday, because you still look tireder than me—doesn't she, Yaya?'

'Well, if you were as full of beans this morning as you have been for the rest of the day, I'm not surprised,' murmured Rosita. 'But I'm afraid you're right. Perhaps we should insist on her spending the day in bed tomorrow.'

He nodded, his eyes gravely inspecting his mother. 'Papá and Yaya can come and play with me... So you can stay in bed and not be tired.'

'I'll do a deal with you,' smiled Beth. 'If you close your eyes now and go to sleep, I'll have a rest to-morrow.'

'You'll have to stay in bed.'

'We'll see, bossyboots,' she chuckled. 'Now, off to sleep—it's late.'

'Did you really mean it about coming back with me?' asked Rosita a few minutes later as they went to the car. 'It's only a couple of days now before Jacey will be out.'

'I know, but there's no need for me to be so close at hand any more,' replied Beth, a feeling akin to dread suddenly gripping her.

'Right, we'll get your things,' said Rosita as they reached the car, the concern in her kindly eyes only increasing Beth's mounting feelings of guilt and dread.

'I... They're already in the boot. I got them when I borrowed your car earlier.'

'I was wrong to encourage you to stay there,' stated Rosita unhappily as she started up the car. 'Just as I suspect I was wrong to tell you those things about Jaime, which—'

'Darling, you told me very little I couldn't have worked out for myself,' Beth cut in. 'And as for my staying at his house, it honestly was the ideal place for me to be before and immediately after Jacey's operation.'

'But not now,' said Rosita, no hint of question in her words.

'No—not now,' agreed Beth, then blurted out, 'Oh,

Rosita, I just wish we could put the clock back to the way things were a couple of weeks ago.'

'And no one could blame you for feeling that way,' sighed Rosita, 'except, of course, Jacey. Despite what he's been through physically, these days that have been so hard on you have brought him great happiness in the knowledge and love of his father.' She flashed Beth a concerned look. 'And this present preoccupation of his with Jaime—it doesn't in any way alter his love for you, darling.'

'I know it doesn't,' Beth conceded, her thoughts churning as she fell into a troubled silence. It was a long while later that she summoned the courage to broach what was on her mind. 'I honestly don't resent Jacey's preoccupation with him... It's Jaime's preoccupation with Jacey that frightens me,' she stated, her words stark with bitterness.

'Frightens you?' echoed Rosita, plainly disturbed.

'Yes, frightens!' exclaimed Beth, her eyes dark with pain. 'Once I was as sure of his love as Jacey is now.'

'Beth, you can't equate the love between a man and a woman with that of a man for his child.'

'Rosita, I know that... Oh, how can I explain it to you?' she pleaded, the tremor of desperation in her voice. 'There were times when I almost convinced myself that I'd been conned by Jaime; that he was no more than a highly skilled philanderer determined to have his cake and eat it.'

'I'm glad you said almost,' muttered Rosita unhappily. 'Because, despite all the apparent evidence to the contrary, I have this feeling in my bones that Jaime Caballeros is no more a womanizer than...than my Miguel was.'

'But it would be so much easier for me if he were!' exclaimed Beth hopelessly. 'I realize you can't possibly be expected to understand…but those things you told me brought everything tumbling into place.' She gave a frustrated shake of her head. 'You'd already told me enough, the day Jacey was admitted, for me to be warned how things would be… But the fact is that I wasn't.'

'Darling, I still maintain that Jaime's the only one who can tell you the whole truth and that anything I've told you can only be classed as hearsay.'

'But it isn't hearsay that he's never married,' Beth said impatiently.

'So what are you saying?'

'I'm just trying to get sorted in my mind exactly how things are… Rosita, I've a feeling that Jaime and this woman he loved must have had some sort of falling out before he met me. It has to have been something like that because I honestly don't believe it was just a case of his being casually unfaithful to her. But when he went back to Barcelona for those few days… Well, you know the outcome of that,' she stated tonelessly. 'Of course he felt guilty about me, once he'd patched things up with her… But it's so easy to see how bitterly he regretted my very existence.' The hatred and scorn she had seen in his eyes that night had had nothing to do with the damningly compromising situation in which he had found her, despite the way he had reacted. She had been instrumental in his betraying his one true love and it had been guilt-ridden loathing that she had seen in his eyes.

'But it doesn't take eyes to see that he has no regrets about Jacey,' protested Rosita.

Beth felt hopelessness seeping through her. Though

she confided more to Rosita than she ever had to another human being, there were still things she felt she must keep to herself, if only for the sake of her pride.

'But for how long?' she asked, tension straining her voice. 'Jacey is the product of what Jaime obviously regards as his betrayal of the woman he loved. Rosita, you saw the way he behaved towards me last night… Could you describe it as anything other than hostile?'

'Beth, I've also seen him behave to you in very different ways at other times,' replied Rosita. 'And last night you were both betraying the strain you'd been under.'

Beth took a shuddering breath. 'If only it were that simple,' she muttered hoarsely. 'As you've probably gathered, I've neither seen nor spoken to Jaime since last night. In fact, I wouldn't have been in the least surprised if he'd made an excuse not to attend that meal… Because he's been doing everything he can to avoid me.' She gazed down in silent misery at the hands clenched tightly on her lap as she accepted she had no option but to swallow her pride and admit the truth. 'Please don't hate me, but…with every encouragement from me he gave in to the sexual attraction he still has towards me…and now he feels nothing but disgust.' Her words ended on a choked sob.

'Hate you, my poor darling?' exclaimed Rosita, aghast. 'There are no conditions attached to the love I have for you, my darling.' She gave a groaning sigh. 'Oh, I should have seen the signs—that morning of Jacey's operation when the maid let me in and I found the two of you fast asleep in one another's arms… That's what I meant when I said I'd seen him behave very differently to you. Naturally, I was initially shocked—which was what led me to speak to you as

I later did—but I also had a strong sense of his pro-tectiveness towards you, his caring. Oh, my poor dar-ling, I should have stayed with you in Palma,' she whispered sadly.

'Not even you could have protected me from my own stupidity,' protested Beth. 'But Jacey—he can and must be protected.'

'Beth, what are you saying?' demanded Rosita, her voice rising with concern. 'Surely you're not thinking of cutting him off from his father once he leaves the clinic!'

'What else can I do?' asked Beth hoarsely. 'I can't just wait until he decides he has to cut himself free from Jacey!'

'Dear God, Beth, you'd have to prove to me beyond any doubt that that was going to happen before I could even consider supporting such an action,' said Rosita, her words sharp with reproof.

'You know I can't do that,' protested Beth numbly. 'But if I were to let Jaime keep seeing him I'd never have a moment's peace... I'd be watching and waiting for the moment when Jaime spurned him. Rosita, how can you ask that of me?'

'I would beg it of you,' retorted Rosita, turning the car into the drive of her house, 'because I most em-phatically don't share your fear that it will happen.' She switched off the engine. 'Beth, I know my in-stincts aren't infallible, but though everything about your relationship with Jaime, both past and present, makes me want to question them now—they tell me you're wrong...terribly wrong.' Her face was drawn with anxiety as she turned to the silent, troubled Beth. 'My love, how could you ever justify to a five-year-old the banishing of his new-found father from his life? The father he loves and who he knows loves him? Beth, how would it affect his unquestioning trust in you?'

'If I knew it would save him from the heartbreak of future rejection, I'd face it… For his sake I'd have to live with the consequences.' The words were torn from Beth in a hoarse cry of pain.

'But you *don't* know,' pointed out Rosita. 'And your way you'd never know if the pain you'd inflicted had been justified.'

It was almost noon the following day when Beth was startled back to wakefulness by the sound of the telephone.

She rose from the sun lounger, checking her watch with a start of surprise as she walked from the shaded patio into the house.

She had tossed virtually without sleep for the entire night, her mind in a restless turmoil of tortured indecision.

'You, young lady, are going to follow your son's advice and do nothing today—you look dreadful,' Rosita had admonished her sternly over the breakfast table. 'Naldo and David are looking after the gallery, so Jacey and I can have the whole day together.'

She hadn't had the energy to argue but even her snatched couple of hours' sleep in the quiet seclusion of Rosita's garden had done little to refresh her physically—and nothing at all to improve her mental state.

'I'm coming,' she grumbled as she reached for the jangling telephone.

'Beth?'

She froze at the familiar, heart-stopping sound of that voice.

'Jaime…'

'You just upped and left… Why, Beth?'

There was something in his tone that penetrated the irrational panic gripping her.

'There's really no need for me to be within such easy reach of the clinic any more,' she replied, astounded by the complete normality of the words and the fact that she hadn't pointed out that it must be as plain as the nose on his face why she had left. 'I'm most grateful to you for having allowed me the use of your home,' she added, and realized immediately how ridiculous the words sounded.

'Don't you think it would be wise for us to talk, Beth?'

Suddenly she knew what was strange about his voice; it was utterly without expression—no shade of tone, no emphasis, just a flat, lifeless delivery of one word following another. She felt the chill of a sickening, mindless fear seep through her. It was as though he had flicked a switch within himself and shut off all emotion.

'Have you seen Jacey?' she asked, unable to stop herself.

'Of course I've seen him.' The switch had been flicked back on. It was another person speaking, vibrant, warm and indulgent as he related his conversations with his son.

As she listened, Beth felt a great part of the fear lifting from her. It was as though he was deliberately proving Rosita right, the blatant message in his tone telling her that his coldness was for her alone, that it would never encompass Jacey. And the residue of fear remaining in her, as she listened to the husky tenderness of his words, was for herself alone. She could never deny Jacey the precious gift of this man's love, but her heart would for ever mourn that it had been snatched so irrevocably from her.

'Though it wasn't Jacey I felt we should speak of,' he continued, the warmth already fading from his voice, 'but what happened between us the other night.'

Beth's heart froze instantly. He had made no attempt to let her down lightly six years ago, and now she had no intention of subjecting herself to the cold, uncushioned words with which he would dismiss her this time.

'Don't be silly, Jaime—we're adults,' she chided, choking slightly on the light-hearted laugh with which she had attempted to accompany her words. 'Under the circumstances it was probably inevitable. Foolish, most certainly, but perfectly understandable.'

She experienced a small stab of anxiety at the complete silence that met her words. Then anger took over. It was obviously fine by him when he was doing the dismissing, but another matter altogether when he was on the receiving end. He had no compunction about having used her, but his male pride, as it had once before, would have considerable difficulty accepting that he had been used in return. And she *had* used him, pride reminded her vengefully, even though vengeance couldn't have been further from her mind at the time.

'If I were you, Jaime,' she continued, stabbing viciously through the silence with the brittle brightness of her tone, 'I'd forget it ever happened. I know I certainly intend to.'

'A night in the arms of a whore—it shouldn't be too difficult to forget.' His words were no longer toneless, savagery lending them vivid colour. 'Except that you're also the mother of my son.'

It was not just the blood that Beth felt drain from her with the impact of those words, it was the remnants of her pride and the last vestiges of her reason.

'Your son, Jaime?' Her tone was glacial. 'That's no problem. Just forget he ever existed. I'll make it easy for you—once he leaves the clinic, you'll never see him again!'

She flung down the receiver and collapsed against the wall. Slowly her body slid downwards until her head was cradled in her arms on the lid of the carved wood chest on which the telephone rested. With no fight left in her, she gave in to long, shuddering sobs of hopelessness.

For the dreamer, trapped in the terrors of a nightmare, there was always the blessed relief of waking... But she had drifted, unsuspecting, into her nightmare six long years ago and had remained locked in its relentless, punishing twilight ever since. It had robbed her of the chance of loving any man but Jaime and now it was threatening the love of the two people she held most dear—her son and Rosita.

She had given herself to him in the obsessive madness of a love that had refused to die... And he had called her a whore, goading her into wielding the only weapon she possessed... One she had never intended using—could never use.

She raised her head from her arms, her eyes gazing blindly at the telephone. For Jacey's sake, she had to undo what she had done.

She rang the clinic, only to be told Jaime was not there. She rang his home and was told the same. She rang the clinic again, asking for the number of his

mobile telephone, and when she rang that she found
it had been switched off.

For several minutes she paced back and forth,
barely aware of what she was doing. Then she picked
up the receiver again. Once more she rang the clinic
and his home, this time leaving messages at both
places for him to ring her.

For a while, unable to stop herself, she continued
pacing beside the telephone, willing it to ring.

Later she returned to the patio and later still returned to her vigil beside the telephone. Her mind was
so geared to the prospect of the telephone ringing that
when the front doorbell did so it was the receiver she
picked up.

'Dear God, what am I doing?' she groaned aloud
to herself, slamming it back down, then turning and
opening the door.

On the doorstep stood Jaime, grim-faced and almost dishevelled-looking. 'Beth, I—'

'Where have you been? I've left messages all over
the place for you to ring me!' she blurted out, almost
hysterical with relief and panic at the sight of him.

'I—'

'Jaime, I was wrong, so terribly wrong to say what
I did to you,' she exclaimed distractedly. 'Of course
you can see Jacey, and see him whenever—'

'Beth, those things I said to you,' he cut in
hoarsely. 'What can I say but that I was out of my
mind? I only hope and pray that you know I could
never have meant what I said…what I called you.'

'I don't want to talk about it!' She turned, stum-
bling back into the hallway as the words burst from
her.

'Damn it, Beth, we *have* to talk about it,' he

snapped, following her inside and closing the door behind him.

'What *is* there to talk about?' she flung at him, any vestige of control deserting her. 'That the fact that you could still want me physically is something you find abhorrent? That it was probably only because you had half a bottle of champagne in you the other night that you were temporarily able to overcome your abhorrence? Well, I've already tried talking to you about that but you hadn't the guts to admit it!'

'For God's sake, Beth, don't—'

'Oh, so I've got it wrong, have I?' She sliced through his protest angrily. 'You were thrilled to bits to discover you could still lust after me, were you? So thrilled, in fact, that you slunk off after spending a night with me, when all—'

'Stop it!' he roared. 'Just how the hell did you expect me to feel?' he demanded, his voice dropping to a hoarse rasp. 'Seeing you after all those years... Discovering I could still want you, despite—' He broke off with an angry shake of his head. 'But those things I said earlier... Forgive me, Beth. I lost my temper and lashed out at you and no one could blame you for the punishment you meted out to me in return.'

'Jaime, there's no point in us carrying on like this,' sighed Beth, feeling utterly drained. 'All I want is for us to try to put the past behind us—to attempt some semblance of friendship, for Jacey's sake.'

'But Jacey *is* our past,' he exploded, then made a noticeable effort to regain control of himself. 'You're right, Beth. If we could put the bitterness of the past behind us, I should feel it a privilege to number you among my friends. But...'

'But what?'

'How will I know you won't change your mind and threaten me with never seeing Jacey again?'

'You'll just have to trust me.'

'And if I can't?'

'What can I say, Jaime?' she asked wearily. 'There's nothing I can do or say to help you believe me.'

'Well, it looks as though I'll just have to find some way to put my mind at rest,' he muttered with a wan smile.

'I hope you succeed,' said Beth. 'Jaime, I... Heavens—I didn't mean to keep you standing here in the hall!' she exclaimed, feeling suddenly gauche and unsure of herself. 'Would you like some coffee—or something cold, perhaps?'

He shook his head, glancing down at his watch. 'It's kind of you to offer, but I've patients to see and I'm already cutting it rather fine.'

Beth nodded. Threatened with losing Jacey, he had dropped everything and sped up here, she thought with a pang of guilt. He opened the front door and stepped out, then turned.

'Jacey told me he'd prescribed a day in bed for you,' he said with an almost diffident smile. 'And he was right to do so... You look worn out, Beth.'

'That's one thing you and he definitely have in common,' murmured Beth, smiling for the first time that day. 'Your tendency to flatter so lavishly.'

He smiled but said nothing, then turned and walked to his car.

Beth closed the door behind him, then leaned against it for several seconds. He was prepared to go to any lengths to keep Jacey in his life now that he had found him, she thought numbly, even if it meant masking his true feelings towards her. She couldn't blame him, but it hurt none the less.

Less than ten minutes after Jaime had left, the phone rang.

'Beth?'

'Jaime?' she exclaimed, puzzled.

'There are some questions I wish to ask you,' he stated abruptly. 'What's the situation regarding men in your life?'

'I beg your pardon?' she gasped, wondering if she could have misheard.

'Is there any man you're in love with or thinking of marrying?'

'I really don't think that's any business of yours,' she snapped. 'Jaime—'

'I've decided it is,' he snapped back, 'so just answer the question.'

Furious, Beth plucked a name from the air. 'Well, Pedro Rivera—'

'Rivera?' he roared. 'I thought anything between you and him was supposed to be a figment of Laurens Morante's imagination!'

'Not necessarily all of it.'

'So what's that supposed to mean?'

'Jaime, would you mind explaining what all this is about?' demanded Beth exasperatedly.

'I asked you a serious question and you fling Rivera back at me!' he exclaimed angrily. 'Hell, he might be a great painter but damn it, Beth, he's not exactly renowned for his mental stability.'

'That's slanderous! Just because—'

'So let him sue me.'

'Oh, for heaven's sake, Jaime,' she groaned. 'This

is ridiculous—I'm not in the least interested in Pedro Rivera, or any other man for that matter!'

'So why did you mention him?'

'Because I have no intention of taking these ridiculous and monstrously prying questions of yours seriously.'

He chuckled; the sound floated from the receiver into her ear and rippled softly through her body, leaving in its wake a hot blast of erotic longing. 'Ah, but you've just let it slip that you're not interested in him or any other man.'

'Jaime, are you going to tell me what all this is about?'

'Of course I am,' he murmured co-operatively. 'You remember I said I'd have to find some way to put my mind at rest?'

'Yes.'

'I've found a solution.'

'And what's that?'

'You could marry me.'

Beth's mind went blank with the shock of his words, making any reaction to them impossible.

'I take it from your voluble response that you need time to think it over,' stated Jaime in the tones of one who could think of no possible reason to think anything over.

'No, I don't,' retorted Beth, striving to sound in control. 'I can only take it you're joking, because the very idea is ludicrous.'

'As I thought,' responded Jaime brusquely, 'you need time to think it over.'

It was several seconds before Beth realized that he had terminated the call and it was with a shaking hand that she returned the receiver to its cradle and sank down heavily on the chest.

She had got it all wrong, terribly wrong, she thought numbly. She had been right to worry, but wrong to do so over Jaime losing interest in Jacey; she now knew that with absolute certainty.

She leaned back against the wall and closed her eyes. If he would go to the lengths of marrying her, of all people, then there could be no lengths at all to which he wouldn't go to keep Jacey. What had he in mind—a brief marriage of convenience, followed by a discreet divorce leaving him with full custodial rights of Jacey? She had little doubt he had the standing and the power to achieve precisely that. But even as the thought tumbled horrifyingly through her mind she was shaking her head in denial of it. Whatever he had in mind, she knew with absolute certainty that he loved Jacey and would never willingly put him through such a trauma.

She thought of Rosita and suddenly felt desperately alone. Rosita had been forthrightly dismissive of her fear that Jaime would lose interest in Jacey and undoubtedly would be just as dismissive of the fear that had replaced it.

'And she'd be right,' Beth groaned aloud. 'I'm being completely paranoid.' Then those coolly uttered words 'You could marry me' reverberated in her head and she found it impossible to be certain of anything.

CHAPTER NINE

BETH frowned as she listened to the flow of words issuing from the telephone receiver, then, in heavily accented English, denied all knowledge of anyone by the name of Beth Miller.

Her expression was troubled as she returned to the garden; it had been the second such call in as many days. Her final assignment, before retiring from modelling, had been for a new range by the cosmetics house to which she had been contracted. It had been shot so long ago that, until yesterday, it had completely slipped her mind that the high-profile campaign was due to be launched this very week.

She gave a shiver, despite the almost oppressive warmth of the day. It wasn't that she had ever deliberately hidden Jacey's existence from the press, she reminded herself; it was simply that they had never discovered it. But if her amazing luck ran out now and they did, she thought grimly, there would doubtless be speculation as to who the father was...

She had known the British press would be around when she had heard of some minor royals holidaying on the island. But she hadn't bargained on one or two of them deciding to branch out and track her down. It had to be that wretched cosmetics campaign that had jogged press interest in her, she decided with deepening apprehension, increased, no doubt, by the fact that they would have heard it was to be her last modelling assignment. But how on earth had they got hold of Rosita's number?

As things were at the moment, it was all she could do to deal with each day as it came, she thought wearily—she needed something like this like a hole in the head. But if they persisted it would probably make things a lot easier if she agreed to just one interview in which she could confirm her retirement from modelling and then appeal to their better instincts to leave her alone. On what grounds, she asked herself wryly—that her son had been ill and had been out of hospital barely a week?

She smiled weakly, well able to imagine the impact of such a statement. Perhaps her previous luck would continue, she thought optimistically; perhaps they would simply persist in trying to link her romantically with men she barely knew—an obtuse single-mindedness on their part that had always worked to her advantage in the past. She shook her head, her optimism fizzling out. Too many people knew about Jacey now for her to rely on that journalistic laxness. Her only hope was that their major prey would keep them entertained enough for them to lose interest in her.

'Mamá, I caught a fish!'

Startled from her thoughts, Beth looked up in the direction of her son's excited voice.

Perched on his father's broad shoulders, he was bouncing with exuberance, while an utterly harassed Rosita winced with unconcealed apprehension at the sight of him.

'If I stand on your shoulders, Papá, I can jump into Mamá's arms,' announced the child, fearlessly struggling to stand upright, but finding his feet imprisoned in the unyielding grasp of his father's hands.

'Perhaps it wouldn't be such a good idea,' chuckled Jaime, throwing Rosita a look that managed to be both wicked and self-congratulatory. 'We wouldn't want to frighten Yaya, now would we?'

'Why stop now?' demanded Rosita waspishly. 'The pair of you have been scaring me half to death all afternoon.'

Depositing his son firmly on the ground, Jaime slipped a cajoling arm round the woman's shoulders, grinning innocently down at her.

'But that was slow for a speed boat—I promise you, Rosita.'

'It was brilliant,' sighed Jacey ecstatically, hurling himself into Beth's arms. 'Papá went really fast and the boat was all lovely and bouncy. Yaya nearly fell overboard, but she'd have been all right—Papá would have saved her.'

'Would he, now?' chuckled Beth, hugging him to her. 'And where's this fish you caught?'

'I put him back—else he'd have died.'

As the four of them trooped indoors, Beth was acutely conscious of the contentment emanating from her three companions.

No one would have been fooled for one moment by Rosita's litany of complaints against the dashing surgeon, who had taken to teasing her mercilessly since she had succeeded in piercing his wall of reserve. It was plain she adored him—as did Jacey. And it was only her respect for Rosita's judgement that had enabled her to relegate her worries about Jaime's motives to the back of her mind, thought Beth nervously—not that they didn't rear up every now and then to disturb her fragile equilibrium.

As did so many things these days, she reminded herself edgily, remembering the first time Jaime had come up after Jacey's discharge from the clinic, when the four of them had gone on a picnic. That night she had cried herself to sleep in the futile realization that it had been one of the happiest days of her life.

Since that day, unwilling to face the aftermath of the pain that such closeness brought, she had found excuses not to join them. But Jacey would take her absences for only so long and she knew that next time she would be hard-pressed to provide an excuse he would accept.

'Why so pensive, Beth?'

She started at the softly spoken words.

'I was just making some tea—or coffee, if you'd prefer,' she replied slightly breathlessly. 'What time do you have to be back?'

'I'm due in theatre at eight. And tea will be fine.'

She nodded, familiar now with his preference for operating either early in the morning or later in the evening, rather than in the heat of the day. Not, she supposed, that the heat would really be a consideration in an air-conditioned theatre.

She felt herself tense as he strolled to her side and leaned against the sink as she busied herself. Sometimes it wasn't too bad; at other times, invariably when they were alone, the illusion of ease they strove to create between them came close to collapse.

'So, where's all this baking that yet again kept you from joining us?' he asked.

Beth glanced up at him, unsettled by the hint of mockery that had crept into his tone. He smiled at her and it struck her how relaxed, almost boyish he looked, lounging in jeans and a T-shirt—a far cry from the decorous surgeon into whom he would soon again transform himself.

'You'll see in a moment,' she replied, deciding that perhaps she had imagined the mockery. 'We're having a typically English tea.'

'What, with scones…and fruitcake?' he asked, parodying the tones of delight Jacey so often used.

Beth nodded, unable to gauge the mood he was in, but suddenly inordinately aware of his nearness. For one suffocating moment she was swamped by the memory of those strong, tanned arms holding her and the maddening excitement that came with the caress of those fingers now drumming idly against the worktop.

'My lawyers are still not happy,' he stated abruptly. 'They—'

'For heaven's sake, Jaime!' she exploded exasperatedly.

The last thing she had expected, when she had flatly refused his startling suggestion of marriage, was the lengths he would go to in his attempts to get her to change her mind, the latest centring on Jacey being his heir. She kept telling him she had no wish even to discuss the subject or anything related to it. But that hadn't deterred him from coming up with increasingly complicated reasons why he, or more recently his lawyers, thought she should. The first time he had mentioned lawyers it had taken every shred of self-control she possessed to hide her panic. The feeling had been so overwhelming that it would have been a miracle if she hadn't betrayed at least a hint of it and she suspected that was what had driven him to turn the whole issue into a bizarre sort of joke. Though how long would he keep it like that, she wondered as yet another of her seemingly innumerable buried worries surfaced, if she actually was pregnant again?

'And as for those lawyers of yours, I'd get rid of them if I were you. There's a simple solution to Jacey inheriting the Caballeros crown jewels that they mysteriously appear to have overlooked. All you have to do is write a will.'

'It's far more complicated than you seem to appreciate,' he muttered stubbornly. 'These "crown jewels" to which you so dismissively refer are not baubles. You have to accept the fact that I'm disgustingly wealthy.'

'And that renders you incapable of writing a will, does it?' she asked, the vividness of her memories sharpening her tone.

He scowled blackly at her. 'Spanish law isn't the same as English law.'

'I don't care how different it is. I've already told you, I don't know how many times, I'm not prepared even to discuss the subject.'

'Beth—'

'For God's sake, Jaime—give it a rest!'

'I was merely going to ask if we were having cream and strawberry jam with our scones,' he retorted infuriatingly, then produced a smile that left her heart skipping several beats.

'Yes—as it happens, we are,' she replied, having to turn away lest his keen eyes spot the warmth stealing across her cheeks.

'Perhaps we should consult Jacey about it,' he said as she finished loading the tea tray.

'About what?' she asked, her blood suddenly freezing.

'About whether or not we should get married.'

'Don't even think about it.' She rounded on him furiously. 'It's bad enough not knowing when you're joking or when you're serious, but—'

'Mamá, why are you being cross with Papá?'

Beth nearly jumped out of her skin at the unexpected sound of her son's voice and turned to find him walking towards them. She reached out to ruffle his hair and found her hand in contact with Jaime's as he too reached out, their intentions identical.

'Has he been a naughty boy?' asked Jacey, his tone anxious.

'Your *mamá* thinks I have been,' replied Jaime gently. 'But I didn't really mean to be. Sometimes I make silly jokes that she doesn't like.' His eyes met Beth's. 'And please believe me, that was all it was—a very silly joke.'

'Well, as long as you promise it won't happen again,' she murmured with a primness she knew Jacey would appreciate, 'you may have your cream tea.'

She turned to pick up the tray and, from the corner of her eye, saw Jacey warningly elbow his father.

'Oh, yes...I promise,' responded Jaime belatedly, and even managed to inject a note of contrition into his tone.

'You promised me you wouldn't mention it again,' accused Beth exasperatedly several days later.

'No, I promised I wouldn't mention consulting Jacey again,' Jaime informed her blandly as he heaved onto Rosita's lawn most of the junk Jacey had loaded into the back of his Aston Martin. 'We're taking your *mamá* for a run in the boat, Jacey, not on safari,' he admonished when his son appeared with even more possessions. 'Now take all that back into the house.'

While the child complied, the man slid back into the driving seat, his expression enigmatic as he looked over at his openly apprehensive passenger. 'OK, today we'll call a truce and I shan't bore you with the mind-boggling complexities of Spanish law,' he murmured, his eyes dropping suddenly to the curve of her mouth.

Beth heard his whispered intake of breath in the instant before he returned his attention to Jacey sauntering back across the lawn. That brief look had left her trembling and confused, and vainly wishing she had never agreed to today's outing.

'Do you plan to get into the car, Jacey?' enquired his father as the child poked his head through the window beside him. 'Or do I have to drive to the harbour with you hanging onto the side?'

It took several moments of explaining from both parents to convince Jacey that his father had not actually been offering him a choice, whereupon a laughing Jaime hauled him through the window and deposited him in the back of the car.

From the moment she had agreed to this excursion, Beth had known it would not be easy for her, but Jacey's obvious delight in her presence brought a large lump to her throat.

On their arrival at the harbour, his face a picture of happiness, the little boy raced ahead, turning every now and then to urge his parents to hurry as they made their way down the jetty.

'Mamá! Papá! Why are you walking so slowly?'

'What a beautiful little boy,' remarked a passing woman in English to her companion.

'And little wonder, with such stunning parents,' responded the second woman.

Beth heard Jaime's soft laughter beside her and found herself looking up into the teasing darkness of his eyes.

'And who are we to disagree?' he murmured in Spanish, the language in which they now usually communicated.

With a laugh he took her by the hand and hurried her towards their impatiently waiting son.

Within moments of speeding out of the harbour, Beth was wide-eyed with alarm to see Jacey being given apparent control of the high-powered craft.

Her alarm subsided considerably when she realized that Jaime was positioned to take the wheel at an instant's notice and gradually she was able to relax, enjoying the sensation of the wind that cooled her face and whipped its dancing presence through her hair. She shaded her eyes against the sun with her hand and watched the two of them, love filling her to overflowing.

From the back the child was a miniature replica of the man, even down to the white T-shirt and denim shorts. It was so easy to see, in the long, perfectly shaped legs of the man, how those of the child would one day develop, just as it was easy to see how the child would grow and fill out to the broad-shouldered athleticism of the father.

She watched as the tall figure slipped out of the T-shirt, and was unable to tear her eyes from the sight of that lean, tautly muscled back, nor her mind from the memory of the feel of that muscled strength beneath her hands. It was her son whose actions tempered the savage ache of those memories as he glanced up adoringly at the man beside him and then removed his own shirt—a gesture that brought a lump to Beth's throat.

She was living on an emotional seesaw, Beth told herself, and wondered how much more she could take. At least she was able to admit to herself that jealousy had been one of the problems she had had to contend with initially—not just of Jacey's obvious adoration of Jaime, but also of Rosita's undisguised affection for him. No, their *loving* him was not the problem... It was more the power over her that their love for Jaime unwittingly gave him. If only he hadn't terrified the wits out of her with his ridiculous suggestion of marriage, she thought wretchedly, perhaps she might have found some means of coping. She gave an unconscious shake of her head as she accepted she was only kidding herself. It would have been one less worry but it wouldn't have altered the fact that she loved him, nor that she might be pregnant.

As though sensing she was in need of it, Jacey turned and blew her a kiss. She blew one back, then hugged her arms around her with a small shiver as she remembered the suddenness of his illness. No matter how insurmountable her problems might seem, the worst was safely behind her, she reminded herself, and wondered if the time would ever come when she could again take for granted the feel of those small, warm arms around her neck and the tickling, often sticky-lipped whispers of love against her cheek.

She watched as her child's face turned up towards that of his father and saw the tall figure stoop to catch the words as they floated from him on the invisible pull of the wind. And again it was as though their hair was one as it mingled, glossy and black, in the clutches of the capricious wind.

As one, man and boy turned to look at her, laughing in carefree delight as they motioned her to join them. As she answered their bidding, Beth was conscious of the infinite complexities of the human mind in its capacity to accommodate both exquisite joy and abject despair at one and the same moment.

Time and again during that afternoon, Beth found herself witnessing the almost uncanny empathy between the two and the knowledge and confidence Jaime had instilled in the child in so short a time.

When they at last arrived back at the jetty, her mind had reached a level of such complete acceptance that, when Jacey was casually handed the mooring ropes by Jaime and told to tie up the boat, she knew it was a task her son would be perfectly capable of carrying out. Jaime Caballeros was proving to be the most thorough of teachers.

With an amused smile, Beth watched the small figure leap confidently onto the jetty, then she set about packing back into the hamper the remnants of the sumptuous lunch Rosita had prepared them. That done, she tackled the discarded T-shirts, suncream bottles and other paraphernalia littering the boat. Tidiness was certainly not one of the lessons Jacey would learn from his father.

'Mamá, these men want to talk to you,' called Jacey excitedly. 'They want to take pictures too—and they've got lots of cameras!'

Beth straightened, sweeping the wind-blown cascade of hair from her face and wishing she hadn't when she heard a familiar whirring and clicking coming from a group of men with their cameras trained on her. All except one, she noted with rising panic. His camera was trained exclusively on Jacey and the child was chattering happily in response to the questions being put to him.

'Beth, what's all this about?' demanded Jaime. 'Is Jacey used to the press?'

She swung round at the sound of those curtly uttered words, her shoulder coming into contact with the silken hair on Jaime's still uncovered chest.

'No—he isn't! Oh, Jaime!' she exclaimed distractedly. 'They don't even know he exists!'

With one powerful leap he was on the jetty and beside the now enthusiastically posturing child.

'Papá, come and have your...' He gave a squeak of indignation as he was swept from his feet and bundled unceremoniously under his father's arm.

'Beth—come!' Jaime called peremptorily, then strode through the half dozen or so pressmen as though they didn't exist.

Beth clambered from the boat, struggling with the hamper but ignoring the outstretched hands and shouted questions.

'Why all the secrecy about the kid, Beth?'

'Is he a love child?'

'Who's the father?'

Then one voice caught her attention above the rest as she battled her way past them.

'His face is familiar... Isn't he the surgeon—Caballeros?' exclaimed the voice. 'Come on, Beth, you can't hope to keep this a secret!'

'Leave her alone!' The words were a roar and Beth felt a hand reach for her, drawing her towards strong, reassuring arms that held her close to a naked, sun-kissed torso.

She turned for a moment, still cocooned in the protection of those arms. 'It was never a secret… I would never have denied the existence of my own son,' she defiantly informed the now silent group. 'It's just that it never occurred to any of you to ask.'

Then she felt herself drawn forwards and bundled into the temporary sanctuary of Jaime's car.

The powerful machine leapt to life, speeding forwards under the palpably angry guidance of its owner.

'They wanted to take a picture of us all together,' piped up Jacey's disappointed voice from the rear. 'It would have been lovely. Why couldn't—'

'Jacey, be quiet,' snapped Jaime.

The child gave a theatrical sigh of protest, but obeyed none the less.

'Jaime,' began Beth, her voice tight and distraught, 'I'm sorry, truly I am. I—'

'What are you apologizing for?' demanded Jaime, giving impatient blasts on the horn as he swung round a corner and startled a group of jay-walking tourists.

'For involving you and Jacey in…in that debacle,' she replied, nervously gripping her seat and praying he would slow down before he killed someone.

'But I *am* involved and nothing can alter that.' His eyes flicked momentarily to her face, his expression softening. 'You don't have to protect me, Beth… Though God only knows how they've remained in ignorance for all these years.'

'I knew there was a press contingent here with those royals,' she blurted out distractedly. 'I should have been prepared for them!'

'We'll discuss this later,' said Jaime, indicating Jacey's presence with a slight movement of his head.

'Jacey, how about if you and I take Mamá and Yaya out to dinner soon?'

'What—to a proper restaurant?' asked Jacey, his interest aroused.

'To the most proper restaurant on the island,' chuckled Jaime as he turned the car into Rosita's drive. His chuckle turned to protesting laughter as two small arms entwined themselves around his neck and an ear-piercing whoop of glee was followed by a smacking kiss on the corner of his mouth. 'Jacey, don't you ever do that again when I'm driving,' scolded Jaime, switching off the engine.

'I'm sorry,' came the small voice from beside him.

'It could have been very dangerous,' pointed out Jaime, then heaved the child into the front of the car and hugged him tightly.

As she followed them into the house, Beth was suffused with the warmth of that spontaneous display of affection. He could be aloof and unapproachable and often downright autocratic, but Jaime couldn't be faulted as a father—a fact that still tended to throw her every now and then.

'I keep hearing what a fine surgeon you are, Jaime,' smiled Rosita as the three of them took coffee on the patio after dinner, 'but I can't help thinking how well you'd have done in paediatrics.'

Both Beth and Jaime regarded her with surprise.

'I don't know why, but I was just thinking about the way you explained everything about his appendicitis to Jacey,' Rosita said. 'When Beth told me about how frank you'd been with him, we were both a little worried. But Jacey and I were talking about it the other day and it's plain that he would have been a very frightened little boy if it hadn't been for you.'

'The credit is Jacey's, not mine,' Jaime told her with a wry smile. 'I've had very little experience with children—on the whole they terrify me. But it's obvious that Jacey is well above average intelligence. In fact, I'm amazed at how enquiring his mind is. He's not afraid of asking questions and he keeps doing so until he has all the facts that he—' He broke off, leaping to his feet in concern as Rosita began choking.

'Rosita, are you all right?' demanded Beth in alarm as Jaime went to the choking woman's side. 'You poor darling, did you—?' She broke off, her mouth gaping in disbelief—Rosita was choking with laughter.

'Forgive me… Sit down, Jaime… Please,' gasped the Spanish woman, wiping tears of mirth from her eyes. 'It was the sight of the pair of you,' she managed, still struggling to curb her laughter. 'Beth sitting there, nodding in total agreement as you, Jaime, played the doting father to perfection.'

'I did?' he asked incredulously. 'I *did*!' he agreed, aghast, the expression of utter bemusement creeping across his face reducing both women to laughter.

'It's because you two are so used to him,' he protested, suddenly defensive. 'He *is* special—' He broke off, waiting with exaggerated patience for Rosita and Beth to compose themselves. 'You have every right to be proud of the way he's turned out…I've been meaning to say that to you both for some time.' He picked up his cup and drained it, plainly embarrassed by the emotion that had crept into his words.

'I'm only glad that you've had the chance to discover just how special he is,' said Rosita huskily, then rose to her feet and went over to him, gently ruffling his hair before reaching for his cup. 'More coffee?'

He nodded. 'Please.'

'Jaime, you're most welcome to spend the night here,' she murmured solicitously.

He leaned back, smiling as he looked up at her. 'Thank you, but no, Rosita. I have an early clinic in the morning.'

After taking coffee with them, Rosita excused herself, saying she had letters to write, and as she disappeared into the house Beth was startled by a soft chuckle from Jaime.

'Rosita has that rare ability to read minds,' he murmured, fixing her with a steady, enigmatic gaze. 'You and I need to talk.'

Beth felt apprehension settle like a concrete block in her stomach. The scene with the press had angered Jaime, yet when Jacey had mentioned it to Rosita earlier he had made light of it. But a tell-tale clenching of his jaw had warned her that she hadn't heard the last of it.

'This business with the press...' he stated evenly.

'They're only here because of the royal holiday,' she said before he could continue. 'The chances are they won't even turn up again.'

'Beth, I'm not a fool,' he snapped. 'It doesn't matter why they're here; the point is that they've dug up what they're bound to regard as a good story. If they turn up again, you'd be better off giving them a statement—one that will satisfy them.'

Beth nodded; she had already come to that conclusion herself.

'It's what you're going to say to them that we need to discuss.'

'I shall tell them the truth. I can't lie, Jaime—and anyway, there wouldn't be any point in doing so now.'

'I wasn't suggesting you lie, Beth. But perhaps it would spare us both a lot of digging into our pasts if you were to tell them we're to marry.'

'This is no longer funny!' she protested, leaping to her feet. 'I've given you what you want regarding Jacey, haven't I—so why can't you leave it at that?'

'What if I can't leave it at that?'

'Oh, for heaven's sake, Jaime, I'm sick and tired of arguing with you!' she exploded, turning on her heel and marching off down the garden. All this almost businesslike talk of marriage, all this playing at happy families, she thought distractedly—was it any wonder she felt as though she was teetering on an emotional knife-edge?

'And if I persist in arguing you'll take Jacey from me—is that it, Beth?' he demanded angrily, appearing beside her.

'No, of course not! I... Jaime, why are you doing this to me?' she pleaded wearily.

'What—asking a woman who hates me to marry me?' he enquired bitterly, flinging himself down on a wooden bench beneath an ancient almond tree. 'I agree, I must be out of my mind,' he muttered, rubbing his hands down his face.

'Jaime, I don't hate you... Not any more,' she said quietly, sitting down beside him. She was living proof that love and hate could sit side by side in a heart, she thought sadly, but now there was only the love left and a futile, aching yearning for what might have been.

'That day when you said that you weren't interested in that weirdo Rivera or any other man—'

'Jaime, what is it exactly that you have against poor Pedro?' she interrupted with an exasperated groan, thoroughly bemused by the turn in the conversation.

'Poor Pedro?' he enquired harshly. 'You think it's OK for him to experiment with drugs and claim it's for the sake of his work, do you?'

'I… Jaime, I'd no idea he was doing that. I—'

'Well, you're either blind or incredibly stupid,' retorted Jaime scathingly, 'or you haven't spent any time in his company during the past couple of years.'

'If you'd let me finish what I was trying to say, you'd have learned that the last time I clapped eyes on the man was long before he became famous.' She rounded on him angrily. 'In fact I haven't seen him since Rosita gave him that first showing at the gallery!'

The dark wings of his brows arched in a parody of astonishment. 'So perhaps you'd care to tell me why you chose to pick on him to use as a…a red herring?'

'A red herring?' echoed Beth. It was about time she stopped being so thoroughly bemused by things he came out with, she told herself angrily, because it wasn't as though she had the slightest idea what went on in his mind regarding anything!

'When I asked you about any men in your life, your immediate reaction was to name one you hadn't seen in years and in whom you hadn't the slightest interest,' he retorted coolly.

'As I pointed out at the time, it wasn't any business of yours,' she snapped.

'But a red herring, I believe, is used to put someone off the scent of something else,' he countered, 'which makes me wonder if there isn't, in fact, someone...a man you might wish to marry?'

'I can hardly believe the tortuous way your mind works!' she exclaimed incredulously. 'There isn't anyone. Jaime—'

'But there could be one day,' he interrupted, his tone harsh. 'I know I'm being thoroughly selfish and unreasonable, but if you were to marry would Jacey's home still be Mallorca? Would his...his stepfather allow him to remain as Spanish as he is now? Who would Jacey call Papá?'

'Those questions will never arise,' blurted out Beth. 'I don't ever intend to marry.'

'But who's to say what might happen in the future?' he asked softly, the merest hint of a taunt in his words.

'That question could also apply to you,' she pointed out. Except that she had the answer. Just as she had, he had lost the only one he would have married for love... The only marriage he could now contemplate was one without that vital ingredient.

'I shall never marry, never have more children,' he informed her woodenly. 'I'd willingly swear an affidavit to that effect.'

'And so would I,' she retorted, apprehension stirring in her as she wondered how he would react to the knowledge that the question of more children might already be out of his control. 'So—there's your problem solved.'

'Your marrying me is the only thing that would solve it,' he snapped, glowering at her in the moonlit dark.

'You're right, you are selfish and completely unreasonable,' she flung at him bitterly, jumping to her feet in agitation. 'Marrying you would solve nothing for me!'

'Nothing?' With an exclamation of anger he leapt up and caught her as she made to walk away. 'Beth!' He swung her round and into his arms, the fire stirring hotly in him igniting an answering flame in her as their mouths clung with the desperation of a hunger that knew no reason.

He slid his hands beneath her lightweight top, a groan escaping him as they spread against the breasts sharpening with eagerness as they swelled to his touch. With a soft, incomprehensible murmur, he drew the top over her head, lowering his mouth to the aching peaks that strained to receive the moist heat of his devouring caress.

'Only you can stop this,' he groaned as they fell in fevered embrace to the grass. 'I know I'm passing the buck,' he choked barely coherently, his hands searching in intimate caress against her body as her own hands impatiently tackled first the belt of his jeans and then the zip. 'But don't stop me... Oh, Beth, don't ever stop me!' he cried out as her trembling hands drew him to her.

'Never,' she moaned distractedly, her body moving to accommodate the hands impatiently ripping aside the flimsy lace of her briefs before arching to receive the hot thrust of his passion with a pulsating quiver of abandon.

She cried out only moments later, when the driving rhythm of his body swelled to a tempo neither could any longer contain. In the moment when the wildness of their passion reached a peak beyond endurance, she grasped his head in her hands, locking her mouth to the groaning moistness of his. And when explosive fulfilment finally rampaged between them it was only the ardour of their kiss that muffled their drowning cries of ecstasy.

'Don't say anything,' growled Jaime, cupping her face in his hands and gazing pleadingly down at her the instant his tortured breathing had subsided sufficiently for him to attempt speech. 'Beth, if you say so much as a single—'

'What could I say?' she managed on what little breath she had, then reached up and stroked her fingers through the dark locks of hair falling across his forehead. 'What could I possibly say?'

They dressed, each dazedly offering help here and there to the other, still too stunned by the ungovernable intensity of what had so swiftly overpowered them even to attempt to discuss it. Then, hand in hand, they made their way round the front of the house to his car.

'Perhaps I should make you coffee before you go,' Beth said, her voice still breathless and barely recognizable to her. But she was grateful when he shook his head.

He opened the car door, then swung round to her with a muttered exclamation. 'Beth?'

'Jaime?'

'No,' he muttered, shaking his head and getting into the car. 'It wouldn't have been a good idea,' he added through the open window.

'What wouldn't have been?'

'Kissing you goodnight.'

Beth's eyes widened, then her heart turned a thousand somersaults as he grinned teasingly up at her.

'Go home,' she chided softly, then turned and walked into the house.

Her excuse was that she loved him and that she was still caught up in the spell of their mind-blowing passion, she told herself almost detachedly—but what was his?

CHAPTER TEN

WHEN Beth staggered into the kitchen at ten o'clock the following morning, it was to find a note from Rosita on the table, telling her that she and Jacey were at the gallery and reminding her that they would be going straight from there to Muro for Jorge's birthday party.

She clapped her hand to her head and winced as it throbbed in painful protest. She had forgotten all about the party.

She went to the dresser and found some aspirins, then dissolved them in water. She was just about to drink the mixture when she hesitated, then tossed it down the sink. Unlike her rejection of the aspirin, the fact that she had spent almost half the night sobbing her heart out had had nothing to do with the likelihood of her being pregnant, she thought wearily. The truth was that were she not she would be desperately disappointed... Which only went to show what a deranged state she was in.

She began pottering around the kitchen, her thoughts darting almost furtively around what had happened between her and Jaime last night. Madness, plain and simple, she informed herself harshly as she began making some coffee. But it was a madness she was going to have to find a pretty speedy cure for, she warned herself, because not only was it tearing her apart mentally, it was beginning to affect her physically as well.

A ring on the doorbell interrupted her thoughts,

something for which she was almost giddily grateful as she went to the hall and opened the door.

'Beth! I can't believe my luck!'

Her mind was a complete blank as she surveyed the man before her; he was of medium height and dressed in a short-sleeved white shirt and lightweight dark trousers. For the briefest of moments she looked at his attractive features without recognition, the thought that she might carelessly have opened the door to a reporter occurring to her in the instant before she let out a cry of delight.

'Cisco? I can hardly believe it! This is such a lovely surprise!'

'And what a surprise,' he laughed. 'I only came here on the off chance that Señora Rubio still lived here and in the hope of getting your address from her.'

'Come in—I've just this minute made some coffee!' exclaimed Beth delightedly, then reached out and hugged him as he stepped through the doorway. 'Oh, Cisco, it really is so good to see you! I was thinking about you just the other day…and remembering what an incredibly good friend you were to me.'

'We've both come a long way since then,' he said, kissing her cheeks before following her into the kitchen. 'You most especially.'

'Forget about me—tell me about you,' she said, noting with pleasure the quiet air of confidence about him—something the boy she had known all those years ago had often seemed to lack. 'You're looking great!'

They took a tray out onto the patio where she picked his brains as to what he had been doing over the years.

'I always knew you were destined to be a highflyer!' she exclaimed delightedly, having no difficulty reading between the lines of his modest account of what was plainly a very successful career with the UN. 'And your wife and little girl—will I be able to see them before you return to New York?'

He shook his head regretfully. 'Not this time, I'm afraid. Fabia and little Julieta flew over to Santander two days ago, to stay with Fabia's parents. I'm joining them tomorrow.'

'I actually had heard you were back here,' sighed Beth, 'but I'd no idea where. What a shame you didn't try tracking me down earlier.'

'I wouldn't have known you were here—let alone that you'd made Mallorca your home—if...' He hesitated, flashing her a somewhat awkward look. 'There were photographs and a piece in one of today's papers...'

'Good heavens, it had gone clean out of my mind!' groaned Beth. 'I take it you're referring to photographs of me and my son and Jaime Caballeros?' She gave a resigned shrug. 'I suppose I should just accept how lucky I am that it's taken the press five years to discover I actually have a son... It must have come as quite a shock to you, though, Cisco,' she added gently.

'It did,' he admitted. 'But had I known all those years ago—' He broke off with a shake of his head. 'I worried about having lost touch with you. In fact, several months later I called here, to find out if Señora Rubio had any news about you. They told me at the gallery that she was in England.'

With no hesitation, Beth told him what had happened; it was the very least she owed him.

'And you made no attempt to contact Caballeros and tell him he was a father?' he asked hoarsely.

'Cisco, what would have been the point?' she asked. 'As far as I was concerned he was married to someone else and the last person I wanted to have anything more to do with. And one of the most difficult decisions I've ever taken was to make Mallorca my home,' she admitted. 'Of course it helped knowing that Jaime worked in Madrid and spent very little time here, making any chance of my ever running into him very small... But my main consideration was Rosita—Señora Rubio. Cisco, there are no words to describe how I feel about her!' she exclaimed passionately. 'To say she's been like a mother to me just isn't enough. But she had the gallery here, which I felt she had been neglecting because of me...and all her friends.'

'I can imagine how difficult a decision it must have been for you,' he said quietly. 'Beth, would you mind if I asked how long ago it was that you eventually met up with Caballeros again?'

'Of course I don't mind,' she said, then told him about Jacey's appendicitis.

'But now you and he are together, are you not?'

Beth shook her head. 'You do know, don't you, that his fiancée died?'

He nodded.

'I honestly believe a part of Jaime died with her,' stated Beth, her voice strained. 'He loves our son...but I don't think he's capable of ever loving another woman.'

Cisco gave her a puzzled look. 'How did he react when you told him the truth about us?'

Beth tensed. 'I...Cisco, the subject has never cropped up between us.'

'So he doesn't know?' he exclaimed, unable to hide his shock.

Beth shook her head, guilt racking her. 'Cisco, what must you think of me?' she whispered. 'I've been unspeakably selfish... Never once thinking of your good name or—'

'Beth,' he cut in gently, 'my reputation doesn't come into it in the least. Though it's a good thing I'd told Fabia about you.' He chuckled. 'You had become quite famous by the time she and I fell in love and it was some time before I realized that she was a little jealous of the pleasure I took in seeing how well you were doing... Which is why I told her the whole story—ever since which she has followed your career far more avidly than I ever did.'

'Oh, I'm so sorry I couldn't meet her!' exclaimed Beth. 'But the next time you're both over we'll definitely get together.'

Cisco nodded, then frowned. 'Beth, the reason I say it's a good thing I told Fabia about you is that we ran into Jaime Caballeros a couple of days after we arrived back here,' he told her quietly. 'If looks could kill, I'd not be here... Not only did I feel that, but my wife did too. Even after all these years, the anger over what he believes happened between us has never died in him.'

Beth shrugged. 'Let's face it, Cisco, his male pride did take quite a hammering that night,' she said, her tone dismissive. 'Now—have you any photographs of Fabia and Julieta on you?'

It was with mixed feelings that she later said goodbye to her unexpected guest. It had been wonderful to see him again and to find him so obviously settled and happy in his life. But his visit had stirred memories of that terrible night, clogging her entire being with them.

She cleared away the tray and squeezed herself

some orange juice, her thoughts still churning disruptively as she returned with the drink to the patio.

Leaning back on a sun lounger, she closed her eyes, a terrible, debilitating anger creeping through her. Jaime must hardly have been able to believe his luck when he had barged in on her and Cisco, she reflected bitterly. But, no matter how callously he had grasped his opportunity, it hadn't stopped him reacting with fury to the idea that she had been unfaithful to him... How could she possibly still love such an out-and-out hypocrite?

She hadn't told Cisco of Jaime's initial conviction that he was Jacey's father, but wondered now what his reaction would have been had she done so.

She drained the glass of orange juice, then flopped back on the lounger, feelings of utter hopelessness elbowing aside her anger.

There was a lesson to be learned from last night and that was that to go on like this would destroy her... Especially if Jaime reacted to his second lapse in the same negative, guilt-ridden way he had to the first. She closed her eyes, a heavy sense of foreboding weighing her down. Her inability to think clearly where Jaime was concerned made rational thought impossible. Tonight, no matter what the consequences, she must tell Rosita everything... Everything.

With that thought alone in her head, she fell into a sleep far sounder than any she had had in the past few weeks.

For almost four hours she slept, and would have continued for several hours more had not a loud, persistent knocking on the front door awoken her.

She groaned aloud as she attempted to stretch, every muscle in her body registering its aching protest.

'I'm coming,' she called out irritably as, after a brief lull, the loud hammering started up again.

She reached the door just as the knocking changed to a continuous barrage of blows. Perhaps, had it not been for the depths of the sleep from which she had just awakened, she might have hesitated before responding to so violent a summons, but as it was she yanked open the door without a second thought. 'Why don't you just kick—'

'I was about to do precisely that,' snapped Jaime, marching in uninvited past her motionless form. 'I've been worried out of my mind... I kept ringing and ringing and got no reply!' He glanced down at the telephone, then accusingly at her. 'Why didn't you answer the damned thing?'

'For no other reason than that I didn't hear it,' retorted Beth, at last managing to shake free from the paralysis that had initially gripped her. 'I was asleep on the patio. But I wish I had heard it—then I could have saved myself having you barging in on me like this!' *And venting your warped disgust on me over last night,* she added in silent fury.

'For God's sake, Beth, I—'

'What's the matter with you anyway?' She cut through his angry protest. 'I don't hear the phone, so you feel obliged to drive from one end of the island to the other and start battering down the door!'

'Francisco Suarez was here this morning,' he stated harshly. 'And he came down to see me straight after.'

Beth felt her mouth go dry. 'So?'

'So?' he echoed, aghast. 'Is that all you can say?'

'For heaven's sake, what else do you expect me to say?'

'Beth, surely it must have occurred to you what he told me?'

'Well, I wish he hadn't,' she flung at him bitterly. 'I don't give a damn about you and your wounded male pride. But I suppose at least poor Cisco will now be spared you glaring daggers at him any time he's unfortunate enough to run into you again!'

'Beth, please,' he begged hoarsely, reaching out and taking her by the shoulders, the bite of steel in his fingers. 'I've had to live with what I believed about you and Suarez for six long years... You have to listen to me!'

'No, *you* can listen to *me* for a change!' she almost screamed at him. 'I don't care how much money you have, how powerful you are,' she gabbled, switching tack as her worst fears took over and spilled from her. 'I'm never going to let you take Jacey from me!'

'For God's sake, Beth, what are you saying?' he rasped, paling. 'How could you even think I'd contemplate something as despicable as that?'

'Because I'm giving you all you say you want regarding Jacey and still you won't leave me alone.' She began struggling frantically against his hold, her pent-up anger bursting free as the increased pressure of his hands rendered her struggles futile. 'Why won't you just leave me alone?'

'Because, God help me, I can't,' he groaned softly.

'No, you can't,' she sobbed wildly. 'And, hypocrite that you are, you take it out on me! Why can't you, for once in your life, be honest with me? Why couldn't you have been honest with me all those years ago and spared me this never-ending nightmare?' she cried out in anguish. 'If you loved so much, how was it you were incapable of recognizing that I loved you every bit as much as you loved her?'

'Beth, please,' he whispered brokenly. 'You're so wrong!'

'Wrong?' she choked, unable to stem what was gushing from her. 'You were my life—was it so wrong of me to expect honesty from you?' A bitter travesty of a laugh burst from her. 'Of course it was! I gave you all the love I ever had to give, yet your first reaction to hearing of the child of that love was that he was Cisco's, not yours!'

His fingers released their vice-like grip as she paused to take more breath to continue her tirade, and he pulled her into his arms.

She collapsed against him, the final dam breaking and spilling its torrents of heart-broken damnation as she sobbed her incoherent accusations against his chest.

Even as he picked her up and carried her into the living room, the litany of hurt and bitterness continued to pour unchecked from her lips.

Awareness began penetrating the tortured chaos of her mind only when he had gently placed her on the sofa, cradling her in his arms as he sat down beside her.

With a choked cry of protest she pulled herself from his hold, recoiling in humiliation from the tear-choked shriek of her own words still echoing in her ears.

'Well, that's more or less it,' she muttered, her tear-ravaged eyes fixed on her tightly clenched hands as the accusations still piled into her mind, negating her claim. 'I suppose that, compared to you, I should consider myself fortunate.' She took a shuddering breath. 'Losing you was like being denied my life—until I learned I was carrying Jacey. For a time he was my only reason for living—then he simply became my life. The wealth that I've achieved and the measure of fame that came with it are nothing to me—no more than a means of providing material comfort for Jacey.'

'Beth, I love you!'

'First you offer me marriage and now you love me!' she exclaimed, her voice hoarse with horror. 'And that's what terrifies me about you... Is there no end to which you wouldn't go to make sure you never lose Jacey?'

'How am I ever going to get through to you?' he exploded. 'Jacey doesn't even come into this! I'm telling you I love you, Beth... You're the only woman I've ever loved!' As the words tore from him, he leapt to his feet and strode to the carved, dark wood fireplace, his back to her as he leaned forward and rested his head against the edge of the mantelpiece. 'The past six years have been a nightmare I'd just about managed to live with until I met you again... And now it's taking me over completely.' He swung round, his face a ravaged mask of pain. 'But the only constant in any of this madness is that I've never loved anyone but you.'

'Madness?' queried Beth dazedly, her head spinning with the effort of trying to find any sense in his nonsensical words. 'Your fiancée,' she protested, grasping the only clear thought she could find among the chaos. 'You loved her... You never loved me!'

'Mariana?' he sighed. 'Oh, yes—I loved Mariana... But not as a man loves a woman. She was literally the girl next door to our place in Barcelona, and I loved her as a sister.'

'Men don't propose marriage to women they love as sisters,' observed Beth in a tense, toneless voice.

'No, they don't,' muttered Jaime, dragging a distracted hand through his hair. 'When we were children we used to joke about the fact that our mothers, who were close, had hopes we would one day marry.' He gave a despairing shake of his head. 'I've honestly no idea when Mariana's feelings for me changed from those of a sister for a brother…but by the time I realized—' He broke off, the look he gave her one of anguished pleading.

'It wasn't until I so reluctantly left you and went back to Barcelona for those few days that I learned the true nature of the poor health Mariana had suffered since childhood… Perhaps, had I mentally stepped back and applied my medical knowledge, I would have realized what was wrong with her long before that terrible day when I learned she had little more than weeks to live… But I hadn't, and when my father gave me the news I was shocked senseless.'

Beth was rooted to the spot by the raw anguish in his words, neither able to speak nor raise her arms in the gesture of comfort she would gladly have offered him.

'It seemed so monstrously unfair; all life's blessings were being lavished on me in the form of you—and there was little Mariana, soon to be denied life itself.'

Barely aware of her actions, Beth rose and walked over to him. In silence she took him by the hand and led him back to the sofa, drawing him down beside her.

'Mariana was never actually told her condition was terminal… There are some people it's probably better not to tell such things—and she was a strangely young twenty-four…'

'But you believe she should have been told?' asked Beth, badly shaken by what she was hearing, but at last finding her tongue.

'I believe she actually knew—though at what point,

precisely, I can't be certain,' he muttered. 'But what I do know is that she couldn't have handled others knowing she knew—that's how Mariana was... And especially not me.' He leaned back his head and closed his eyes. 'Two days after I arrived in Barcelona, my father and I were invited round to Mariana's parents' for dinner... I hadn't seen her since I'd heard the news and it was still all so raw in me that I found it impossible to behave normally.

'I am aware that I was probably far more affectionate to her than I would usually have been. After the meal we went for a walk in the garden, just the two of us, and she asked me if I'd found myself a good woman yet... It was a sort of joke between us—' He broke off with a shuddering sigh.

'How could I possibly have told her about us?' he demanded hoarsely. 'I was feeling almost guilty that you and I had so much... So I ended up saying that no one would have me and she said, "Except me". To this day I have no recollection of who said what after that, but the result was that when we returned to the house Mariana announced our engagement to my father and her parents. They were all stunned, naturally—but not nearly as stunned as I was...

'It was only a while later that my uncle, Filipe, rang—he and Mariana's father were old friends. It's probably next to impossible for you to understand how it was, but there we all were, pretending to celebrate, when, apart from perhaps Mariana, we couldn't have felt less like celebrating. Then, as I said, Filipe rang; he knew nothing about Mariana's illness and because she was there, able to hear every word, her father had no option but to give him the so-called good news.' Jaime turned to Beth, stark pleading in his eyes. 'Beth, I swear to God that had I realized

Filipe was ringing from the hotel I'd have found a way of calling him back immediately and putting him in the picture.'

'But you came back that same night,' said Beth, her words devoid of any expression.

'Of course I came back!' he exclaimed hoarsely. 'When you told me what was going on at the hotel and hung up on me...I was devastated. Beth, I felt trapped and confused and in desperate need of you. I had this crazy hope that you'd understand... That you'd agree to wait for me while I saw this unhappy charade through.'

Beth became conscious of the hot wetness of tears on her cheeks and rubbed at them with the back of her hand. Of course she would have understood; of course she would have waited till the end of time for him.

'Please, Beth, don't cry,' he begged softly, turning and drawing her into his arms. 'I had to tell you it all, so that you could understand what had happened and know that my feelings for you had never changed. Listen to me, I beg you,' he whispered, rocking her gently as a sob choked from her. 'I love you.' He repeated the words, this time in English, then again in Spanish. 'Are you listening? Are you hearing?' he demanded huskily, his mouth placing feverish butterfly kisses on her tear-stained face. 'Tell me that you believe it—that I love you and only you,' he breathed against her mouth. 'Tell me that—nothing more, just for this moment.'

'Jaime, oh, Jaime,' she whispered brokenly. 'I'd have waited for ever for you, if only I'd known. I hated you for not trusting me, yet where was my trust in you? I behaved so stupidly, so vindictively... How could you possibly love someone as selfish and—?'

'Just tell me!' he protested, his arms tightening fiercely.

'That I believe you love me?' she asked, feeling as though something was about to explode in her.

'Yes!'

'I do believe it,' she whispered, the words catching in her throat as something wondrous thundered to life within her. 'But—'

'No,' he protested unsteadily, his look that of a man sleep-walking. 'Just for this moment, no buts… We'll deal with them later.'

'You want me to wait till later to tell you how much I love you?' she teased tremulously, oblivious of the tears coursing down her cheeks. 'I love you now as I did then.' She reached up a hand, her fingers caressing his cheek before they crept into the gleaming darkness of his hair. 'As I've always loved you—with all my heart, with all the life there is in me.'

With a groan he caught her to him, burying his face in the curve of her neck, rocking her against him as his lips chanted a soft litany of love against her skin. Wordlessly they gave in to a mutual need to hold and be held, a need born of a love so intense that for the moment it was beyond sexuality.

She felt the heat of his breath against her neck and then, as a long, shuddering sigh tore from him, the scalding sensation of tears against her skin. It was only when she felt his face turn from her that her arms relinquished their frantic hold and her hands cradled his head against her, her fingers caressing softly in his hair.

'Hell, there has to be a limit to this,' he groaned, lifting his head, then smiling up at her through the tears glistening on his face. 'Even if it is for you.'

Her puzzled expression reflecting her worry that

she might have reason to fear for his sanity, Beth watched him unselfconsciously wipe aside those tears with the back of his hand in a gesture that was pure Jacey.

He grinned. 'It seems a lifetime ago that you told me there could be no shame in tears shed for love... And, as you can see, I love you by the bucketful. Oh, Beth—how I love you!' His laughter was filled with delight as he lifted her, then swung their bodies round so that they lay together along the sofa, he on his side and peering down at her.

Beth wasn't conscious of holding her breath; she was too absorbed with the blinding glare of happiness in the eyes gazing down into hers, trapped in their enchantment as she had been from the first. Mesmerized, she watched those green-specked eyes deepen to the stormy darkness of passion as they lingered caressingly on her mouth. Slowly he lowered his head until their lips all but touched.

'Now we come to the buts... To last night, for instance,' he whispered huskily, each word he uttered bringing his lips into electrifying contact with hers, 'and that other night when we kept making love—' He broke off with a groan, his mouth claiming hers with an insatiable hunger.

Where moments before they had held one another in a need that was almost platonic, passion now flamed violently between them.

With no warning he pushed her from him with a groan, the scowl into which he tried to compose his features deteriorating into a grin. 'I think you'll agree that we have far too much explaining to do to Rosita and our son without their walking in on us making love.' Grinning teasingly, he swung his legs off the sofa, then repositioned both Beth and himself until they were sitting chastely side by side. 'Now, that's better, isn't it?' he murmured piously.

'Safer, perhaps,' muttered Beth uncooperatively, need for him still pounding through her, 'but certainly not better.' She glanced up at him, frowning suddenly. 'Jaime, I...I'm still having difficulty believing any of this is really happening. My head's a complete jumble.'

With a laugh of soft contentment, he slipped his arm around her and pulled her against him. 'There's quite a bit of jumble buzzing around in my head too,' he told her gently. 'I keep telling myself that a day is going to come when the horrors that are still so fresh will be no more than a dull ache—a day when we have both accepted the miracle of our being together as nothing but a beautiful right that is ours for ever.'

As though suddenly unable to cope with happiness of such magnitude, Beth found her mind throwing out frantic warnings about taking it for granted with so much still remaining unsaid.

'Jaime, we still haven't dealt with the buts,' she whispered, fear suddenly numbing her. 'All the lies I've told you...'

'Cisco Suarez told me everything,' he murmured, catching her hand and raising it to his lips. 'But I have to admit it will be a long, long time before I can even begin to think rationally about that hellish night,' he said, his voice dropping to a hoarse whisper. 'At first I hadn't given the slightest credence to that ghastly June's ranting accusations against you. But when I barged open the door... When I saw the two of you lying there and heard you confirm what every instinct I had told me not to believe... To say I was consumed by a madness of jealous rage doesn't begin to describe what I felt.'

'I wanted to hurt you,' she whispered, feeling as though she was suffocating.

'To say you succeeded is the understatement of the century. That hurt is something that I've been living with from that moment until today when Suarez freed me from it,' he muttered, then gave a dazed shake of his head. 'But when I leapt to the conclusion that he was Jacey's father—weren't you tempted to tell me then?'

'I was too angry. Later it was no more than mis-placed pride that stopped me. I felt that if I'd told you the truth it would have been tantamount to admitting how desperately you had hurt me... How desperately I still loved you.'

'Dear God, when I think of the years we've wasted!' he exclaimed, a terrible bitterness in his tone. 'For the short while Mariana was still alive, I man-aged to keep going for her sake—' He broke off with an angry shake of his head. 'But it was as though there was nothing to keep me in check once she had gone. I had accepted that I could never love again, and openly admitted it, but it was as though I was trying to prove I was wrong. And in the process I treated many women in a way I shall regret till the day I die. I was so consumed with thoughts of you that it didn't even occur to me that most people ex-cused my appalling behaviour as grief over losing Mariana.'

Beth buried her head against him, barely able to speak, but knowing she had to. 'I don't think I ever consciously admitted to myself that I could never love again,' she began hesitantly, 'but I didn't have to... The moment I became even remotely interested in a man, something would switch off in me.' She paused, taking a deep breath to enable her to continue. 'Jaime, you're the only man who has ever made love to me.'

'Darling, you're shaking,' he protested, the significance of her words seemingly lost on him.

'Because I'm dreading how you might react to an indirect lie I told you,' she stated woodenly. 'One you'll probably regard as unforgivable.'

She felt his body tense suddenly, then heard the breath expel from him, hissing softly through clenched teeth.

'A woman who last made love around six years ago would not have the need to be protected against conception,' he stated quietly.

'No, she wouldn't,' managed Beth, scarcely able to breathe.

'But you, my darling, made no claim to being on the pill or any other form of contraception. You merely said it was all right for me not to use anything. And, if you remember, I didn't ask you to clarify what you were saying.'

'Would you mind if I asked you to clarify what you're saying now?' she asked dazedly, the pessimist in her refusing to let go.

'I doubt if I can,' he sighed. 'There was no real consciousness in my reaction, just a vague, crazily irrational hope. The truth is that any thought I ever seem to have in connection with you is either crazy or irrational—or both. But deep down there was a part of me that sensed, despite everything, that you still loved me. I was still trapped in the lies of the past when I told you nothing mattered that night. Beth, I was swallowing my pride and trying to tell you that what I believed had happened between you and Suarez didn't matter to me any more—' He broke off with a dazed shake of his head. 'I'd performed that emergency Caesarean section that day,' he whispered, burying his face against her neck. 'And it had an effect on me that shook me to the core. That woman had been in a bad accident; she couldn't be moved because of a badly broken leg and her husband was beside himself with worry... But I've never seen anything like the joy on their faces once they held their baby safe and whole in their arms. I found myself being torn apart inside for the lonely, loveless pain in which you had given life to our son. That night, crazily and irrationally and without even consciously acknowledging it, I wanted to believe that our love-making would create another child, one that this time would be born neither in loneliness nor the lack of its father's love.'

'But you left the next morning without so much as a word,' protested Beth, the pessimist in her making one last stand in the face of defeat. 'And when you came back in the afternoon...'

'You rounded on me as though you hated me, demanding to know what I was doing there and so rightly accusing me of having problems about the night before,' he sighed. 'Hell, I had problems all right, but wanting you was the least of them. Though I would probably have died rather than admit it, from the moment I saw you standing in my office I knew in my heart of hearts that I still loved you—and it horrified me rigid. But that night, when I held you in my arms, it was as though I'd been hurtled back to a time when your love for me was a certainty that it wouldn't have occurred to me to question.' His arm tightened around her. 'God only knows how many times I went back to you before I left that morning, wanting to wake you and hold you in my arms and tell you how much I loved you. Reason told me I couldn't do it and then just dash off, as I would have had to... But I wish to God I'd ignored it, because for the rest of the day I kept having flashbacks of that last terrible night... I worked myself into such a state that I was almost deranged, and the idea that you could possibly love me seemed ludicrous—' He broke off with a shudder. 'Hell, even thinking about this is depressing me,' he groaned. 'Can't you say something to shut me up?'

'How about I love you?' murmured Beth, having serious problems with her breathing.

'That might just do the trick,' he chuckled.

'Oh, Jaime,' she choked, hovering between tears and laughter as a bubble of wonderment burst within her. 'I love you, I love you, I love you!'

'That's exactly what the doctor needed,' he laughed. 'And something else he's desperate to hear is when we are likely to know if our sortie into planned parenthood has paid off,' he teased softly, hugging her suffocatingly to him.

'Soon, very soon,' she promised with a shiver of contentment.

'I had rather a strong sixth sense about that first time,' he mused teasingly. 'Though last night in the garden...'

'What about it?' enquired Beth innocently.

'I think we'd better change the subject,' he groaned, 'and arrange to have you tested right away.'

Beth flung her arms around him.

'Beth,' he growled, drawing back from her impassioned embrace.

'Yes?' she murmured lazily, thrilling to the sultry change taking place in the eyes burning down into hers.

'If you don't stop leaping on me in this lascivious

way, I'll be forced to heave you out onto the road—armed with a handful of change.' He chuckled as her eyes widened in questioning bemusement. 'Then you'll have to find a pay phone to ring me from—so that I can ask you if you love me enough to—'

'I love you enough for anything,' she interrupted delightedly.

'Enough to marry me soon—like tomorrow?' he enquired huskily, his mouth hovering temptingly close to hers.

'But of course,' she replied breathlessly. 'And I'll leave you to deal with the press.'

'It's a deal,' he agreed, in tones identical to hers.

'One thing troubles me, though,' she sighed softly, their lips now almost touching. 'Why the big delay till the wedding?'

'That's a very good question,' he whispered distractedly before his mouth enthusiastically claimed hers.

Seconds later he gave a groan of exasperation at the sound of the crunch of wheels on the drive. 'Saved by the cavalry,' he chuckled ruefully as a door slammed shut. 'Hell!' he exclaimed, suddenly sitting upright. 'What if Rosita decides she doesn't want me as a surrogate son-in-law?'

'I'm afraid you'll be given the boot, *señor*,' grinned Beth, ruffling his already tousled hair.

He was placing a kiss on the hand he had just removed from his head when the living-room door burst open. Jacey stood there, the disbelief on his small face as he looked from his mother to his father turning to hope, then a silent, tremulous joy.

'You can believe what you see, my son,' Jaime told him softly, stretching out a hand to the speechless child. 'Sometimes grown-ups can be very foolish, but your *mamá* and *papá* have always loved each other—and you, our darling Jaime Carlos, are living proof of that love.'

'Don't cry, my darling,' begged Beth as the small form clambered onto the sofa to join them, tears streaming down his cheeks as he buried his face against his father's chest.

'I'm *not* crying,' he protested indignantly. 'I'm being very happy! Will we always be together now? For ever and ever?'

'For ever and ever,' promised Jaime huskily. 'From now on we'll always be a proper family—you and Yaya and Mamá and me... Where is Yaya?'

'I'm here,' declared an unsteady voice from the door, and Rosita marched purposefully towards them. 'I've been expecting this, because in my bones I knew you two were a pair of...of blind idiots! All I can say is thank God that you've at last come to your senses. And when is the wedding?'

'See, she can't wait to have me as a son-in-law.' Jaime smirked at Beth. 'And about the wedding, Rosita—I'm afraid there may be the need for inordinate haste where that's concerned.'

'Jaime!' groaned Beth, blushing to her roots.

'Is Papá being naughty?' demanded Jacey, his tears replaced by a look of blissful contentment.

'I'm sure he is,' chortled Rosita. 'But I dare say we'll be able to keep him in hand.' She surveyed the three of them on the sofa, shaking her head in mock exasperation and seemingly oblivious of the tears sliding down her cheeks. 'I'm off to make some tea,' she announced gruffly.

'You see,' breathed Jacey triumphantly. 'Yaya was being very happy too.'

'You missed the best bit,' Jaime told him softly,

his eyes capturing Beth's across their son's head and bombarding her with messages of love. 'It was like a cloudburst in here a while ago when your mother and I were being very happy.'

'I'm still having difficulty believing this much happiness is possible,' sighed Beth, her eyes misty with their answering messages of love.

'Well, you'd better believe it, my darling,' stated Jaime firmly, 'because this time it's here to stay.'

His words were a promise that her heart knew without question he would always keep.

MILLS & BOON®

Next Month's Romances

♡

Each month you can choose from a wide variety of romance novels from Mills & Boon®. Below are the new titles to look out for next month from the Presents™ and Enchanted™ series.

Presents™

JOINED BY MARRIAGE	Carole Mortimer
THE MARRIAGE SURRENDER	Michelle Reid
FORBIDDEN PLEASURE	Robyn Donald
IN BED WITH A STRANGER	Lindsay Armstrong
A HUSBAND'S PRICE	Diana Hamilton
GIRL TROUBLE	Sandra Field
DANTE'S TWINS	Catherine Spencer
SUMMER SEDUCTION	Daphne Clair

Enchanted™

NANNY BY CHANCE	Betty Neels
GABRIEL'S MISSION	Margaret Way
THE TWENTY-FOUR-HOUR BRIDE	Day Leclaire
THE DADDY TRAP	Leigh Michaels
BIRTHDAY BRIDE	Jessica Hart
THE PRINCESS AND THE PLAYBOY	Valerie Parv
WANTED: PERFECT PARTNER	Debbie Macomber
SHOWDOWN!	Ruth Jean Dale

On sale from 13th July 1998

H1 9806

Available at most branches of
WH Smith, John Menzies, Martins, Tesco,
Asda, Volume One, Sainsbury and Safeway

Penny Jordan

COLLECTOR'S EDITION

The *Penny Jordan Collector's Edition* is
a selection of her most popular stories,
published in beautifully designed volumes
for you to collect and cherish.

*Available from Tesco, Asda, WH Smith, John Menzies,
Martins and all good paperback stockists, at £3.10 each -
or the special price of £2.80 if you use the coupon below.
On sale from 1st June 1998.*

Valid only in the UK & Eire against purchases made in retail outlets and not in
conjunction with any Reader Service or other offer.

30ᵖ OFF
COUPON
VALID UNTIL: 31.8.1998
PENNY JORDAN COLLECTOR'S EDITION

To the Customer: This coupon can be used in part payment for a
copy of PENNY JORDAN COLLECTOR'S EDITION. Only one
coupon can be used against each copy purchased. Valid only in the
UK & Eire against purchases made in retail outlets and not in
conjunction with any Reader Service or other offer. Please do not
attempt to redeem this coupon against any other product as refusal
to accept may cause embarrassment and delay at the checkout.

To the Retailer: Harlequin Mills & Boon will redeem this coupon at
face value provided only that it has been taken in part payment for
any book in the PENNY JORDAN COLLECTOR'S EDITION. The
company reserves the right to refuse payment against misredeemed
coupons. Please submit coupons to: Harlequin Mills & Boon Ltd.
NCH Dept 730, Corby, Northants NN17 1NN.

9 904170 250306 >

0472 01316